DISCOVERIES

Senior Author
William K. Durr

*Senior Coordinating
Author*
John J. Pikulski

Coordinating Authors
Rita M. Bean
J. David Cooper
Nicholas A. Glaser
M. Jean Greenlaw
Hugh Schoephoerster

Authors
Mary Lou Alsin
Kathryn Au
Rosalinda B. Barrera
Joseph E. Brzeinski
Ruth P. Bunyan
Jacqueline C. Comas
Frank X. Estrada
Robert L. Hillerich
Timothy G. Johnson
Pamela A. Mason

HOUGHTON MIFFLIN COMPANY   BOSTON

Atlanta   Dallas   Geneva, Illinois   Lawrenceville, New Jersey   Palo Alto   Toronto

Acknowledgments

For each of the selections listed below, grateful acknowledgment is made for permission to adapt and/or reprint original or copyrighted material, as follows:

"Birthdays," adapted from *Little Owl, Keeper of the Trees,* by Ronald and Ann Himler. Text copyright © 1974 by Ronald and Ann Himler. Reprinted by permission of Harper & Row, Publishers, Inc.

"Changing," from *Yellow Butter Purple Jelly Red Jam Black Bread,* by Mary Ann Hoberman. Text copyright © 1981 by Mary Ann Hoberman. Reprinted by permission of Viking Penguin Inc.

"Daniel's Duck," adapted from *Daniel's Duck,* by Clyde Robert Bulla. Text copyright © 1979 by Clyde Robert Bulla. Reprinted by permission of Harper & Row, Publishers, Inc. and Curtis Brown, Ltd.

"The Giant Who Threw Tantrums," adapted from *The Book of Giant Stories* by David L. Harrison. Copyright © 1972 by David L. Harrison. Reprinted by permission of McGraw-Hill Book Company.

"It's Not Fair!" adapted from *The Oldest Kid* by Elaine Knox-Wagner. Copyright © 1981 by Elaine Knox-Wagner. Reprinted by permission of Albert Whitman & Company.

"Little Puppy," from *Navajo Indian Poems,* transcribed by Hilda Faunce Wetherill. Reprinted by permission of Ruth Wattles.

Continued on page 319.

Printed in the U.S.A.

ISBN: 0-395-37606-8

EFGHIJ-D-943210/8987

Contents

Magazine One

Magazine Two

Discoveries
Magazine One

Contents

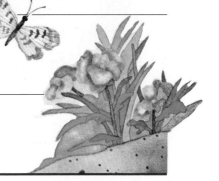

SAY HELLO, VANESSA

by Marjorie Weinman Sharmat

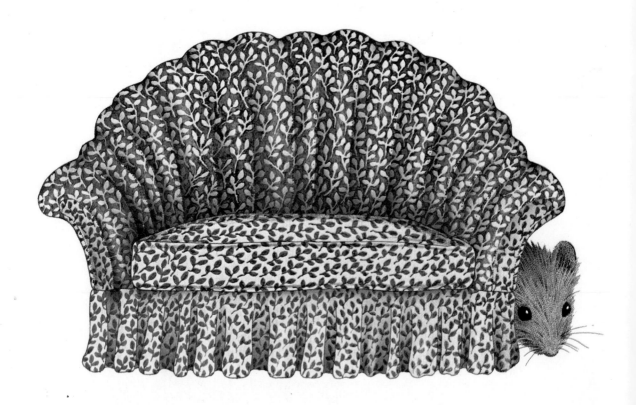

Vanessa Mouse is too shy to say hello.
How will she find a friend of her own?

Vanessa Mouse lived with her mother and father in a fine, old house.

Mrs. Mouse had many friends. When they came to visit, Vanessa hid. Vanessa would look out from behind the sofa because she was very shy.

"Say hello, Vanessa," said her mother, but Vanessa wouldn't say hello.

When Mr. Mouse's friends came over, Vanessa sat in a corner and didn't look up.

"Look up, Vanessa," said her father, but Vanessa wouldn't look up.

No friends came over to see Vanessa because Vanessa didn't have any friends.

"Vanessa, dear, you don't have one friend," said Mrs. Mouse sadly. "You don't even have a now-and-then friend, or an every Sunday friend. You don't have a rainy day, sit-by-the-window friend. There's nobody."

"Trying to make friends must be the scariest thing in the world," said Vanessa.

"Well, the first time might be a little scary," said Mrs. Mouse, "but why don't you try it?"

The next day Vanessa went to school and took her seat in class behind Quincy Moose.

"It's wonderful hiding here behind Quincy Moose," thought Vanessa.

Mr. Mitchell, the teacher, said, "Today we'll start with spelling."

He looked at Andrew Aardvark. "Andrew, how do you spell *country*?"

"Does it start with *k*?" asked Andrew.

"No, I'm afraid it doesn't," said Mr. Mitchell. He looked at Craig Badger. "Can you spell *country*, Craig?"

"Does it end with an *e*?" asked Craig.

"No," said Mr. Mitchell, "it doesn't. Who knows how to spell *country*?"

Vanessa started to raise her hand. "I know how, I know how," she said to herself. Then she put down her hand. "But I can't because everybody will look at me. Maybe I'll spell *country* some other day."

After class, everyone but Vanessa got
together in little bunches and groups ...
everyone but Vanessa, who was all alone.

"Bunches and groups, bunches and groups,"
thought Vanessa. "Everyone has enough
friends already so they don't need me."

When she got home, her mother asked,
"Well, Vanessa, did you make a friend today?"

"No," said Vanessa, and she told her mother
about bunches and groups.

"I see," said Mrs. Mouse. "Tomorrow if you
look hard enough, you'll find someone who
is alone. Then you can go up and say hello."

"I'll try that," said Vanessa.

At school the next morning, Mr. Mitchell
asked, "Who has learned to spell *country*?"

Everyone looked around.

"A time like this might never come again,"
thought Vanessa.

Vanessa started to raise her hand,
but she put it down again.

"Maybe tomorrow
I'll do it," she thought.

When class was over, Vanessa saw
Laura Goat standing alone against a wall.
Slowly Vanessa went up to Laura.
Vanessa whispered, "Hello."
"What?" asked Laura.
"Hello," whispered Vanessa.
"What?" asked Laura again.
Vanessa walked away, and then she ran
home to her mother.

"I said hello but I didn't make a friend," said Vanessa.

"Saying hello usually works," said Mrs. Mouse.

"It didn't for me," said Vanessa. "I went up to Laura Goat and very quietly said hello, but all she said was *what?*"

"Try again tomorrow with someone else," said Mrs. Mouse, "and speak a little louder."

"I'll try," said Vanessa.

Vanessa hurried to school the next morning and took her seat behind Quincy Moose.

Mr. Mitchell asked, "Who can spell *country*?"

"*C-o-u-n-t-r-y,*" Craig Badger spelled.

"Oh, no," thought Vanessa. "Well, anyway, the day isn't over yet."

After school Vanessa looked for someone
who was alone. At last she saw Sigmund
Toad counting the pencils in his pencil box.
Vanessa walked up to him.

"HELLO!" she shouted.

Sigmund dropped
his pencil box.

"HELLO!" she shouted again.
Sigmund put his hands over his ears
and hopped away.

That night Vanessa told her mother about her new hello.

"Maybe a medium hello will work," said Mrs. Mouse.

"I don't want to try any more hellos," said Vanessa.

The next day Vanessa's mind was made up. "Today I will not say anything, not anything at all!" she said to herself.

She took her seat behind Quincy Moose.

Mr. Mitchell said, "Does anyone know how to spell *tooth*?"

"Oh!" thought Vanessa. "I do!"

Mr. Mitchell looked around.

Vanessa felt hot. She was thinking, "*Tooth* is such a great word to know how to spell, and I know how to spell it!"

Suddenly Vanessa raised her hand high ... and then higher. She waved it and said, "I can spell *tooth*! *T-o-o-t-h*!"

"Right," said Mr. Mitchell.

Everyone was looking at Vanessa, but she didn't mind.

After class was over, Vanessa gathered
up her books.

Suddenly Quincy Moose turned around.
"I wish I knew how to spell *tooth*," he said.
"I wish I knew how to spell *moose*."

"*Moose* is easy," said Vanessa. "It's
like *mouse* but it has an *o* where the *u* is."

Vanessa and Quincy walked out of class
together and talked about *mouse* and *moose*.

"That was fun," said Quincy. "Let's do
it again."

"Do you want to come to
my house?" asked Vanessa.

"Sure," said Quincy.

Vanessa and Quincy walked
to Vanessa's house.

They saw Mr. Mitchell.

"Hello, Mr. Mitchell," said Vanessa.

They saw Andrew Aardvark.

"Hi there, Andrew," said Vanessa.

They saw Craig Badger.

"How are you, Craig?" said Vanessa.

They saw Laura Goat.

"Hi, Laura," said Vanessa.

They saw Sigmund Toad.

"Nice day, Sigmund!" said Vanessa.

When Vanessa got home, she ran
into the house. "Mother! Mother! I
brought someone home!"

"I'm Quincy Moose. *M-o-o-s-e*," said Quincy.
"And you must be Mrs. Mouse. *M-o-u-s-e*."

"And you must be Vanessa's friend,"
said Mrs. Mouse.

"That's who I am!" said Quincy.

"A friend is fun to have," said Vanessa.
"And best of all is an everyday,
sit-by-the-fire-and-talk friend."

Thinking It Over

Comprehension Questions

1. How did Vanessa Mouse finally find a friend?

2. What things did Vanessa do that showed she was very shy?

3. What things did Vanessa try that *didn't* work in making a friend? Why do you think they *didn't* work?

4. What else could Vanessa have done to make new friends?

Word Watch

usually	whisper	high
speak	drop	shout

1. Which word means *to speak softly?*
2. Which word means *to speak loudly?*
3. Which word means almost the same as *often*?
4. Which word means the opposite of *pick up*?
5. Which word means almost the same as *talk*?
6. Which word means the opposite of *low*?

Making Friends

What are some ways a shy person could make a friend? Write about your ideas.

CHANGING

by Mary Ann Hoberman

I know what *I* feel like;
I'd like to be *you*
And feel what *you* feel like
And do what *you* do.

I'd like to change places
For maybe a week
And look like your look-like
And speak as you speak
And think what you're thinking
And go where you go
And feel what you're feeling
And know what you know.

I wish we could do it;
What fun it would be
If I could try you out
And you could try me.

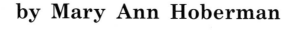

Predicting Outcomes

When you read, you can sometimes figure out what might happen next if you think about what you have already read. The story below tells about a girl named Tess. Read it and think about what is happening to help you decide what might happen next.

On the way to the pet shop, Tess and her mother talked about buying a pet. Tess watched closely as the owner of the pet shop put three kittens on the floor. One kitten ran to Tess and licked her finger. When Tess picked up the little kitten and held it close, it purred happily. "I know what I want to do!" Tess told her mother.

Which of these three things do you think will happen?

1. **Tess will go home without any pet.** Probably not, because Tess and her mother went to the pet shop to get a pet.

2. **Tess will ask the pet shop owner if she can see other kittens.** Probably not, because Tess said she knew what she wanted to do.

3. **Tess will go home with the kitten that she picked up.** Yes, this will probably happen, because this kitten licked Tess and purred. Tess picked it up, held it close, and told her mother, "I know what I want to do."

To find the right answer, you needed to think about what you knew about pets and about what you were told in the story.

Now you are going to find out more about Tess and her new pet. Use what you know about pets and what you are told in the story to figure out what might happen.

Tess put her new kitten on the kitchen floor while she went to get some milk for it. Just then her older brother, Eric, and his dog, Bruno, walked into the room. Bruno stopped, sniffed, and stared at the kitten. The fur on the kitten's back stood straight up. Eric told Tess to hold the kitten and pet it. Then he brought Bruno near the kitten. The dog and the kitten sniffed each other. Bruno licked the kitten and wagged his tail, so Tess put the kitten back on the floor.

Do you think the new pet kitten and Bruno will become friends? Think about what you already know about pets and what you were told in the story.

Skill Summary

It will help you enjoy and understand what you are reading if you think about what might happen next as you read. Think about what you already know and about what the author tells you.

A Special Trade

by Sally Wittman

Nelly and Bartholomew are neighbors and good friends. What is their special trade?

Bartholomew is Nelly's neighbor. When
Nelly was very small, he would take her
for a walk every day in her stroller to Mrs.
Pringle's vegetable garden.

Bartholomew never pushed too fast.
When they were coming to a bump,
Bartholomew always told Nelly.

"Hang on, Nell!" he would always
say. "Here's a bump!"

Nelly would shout "BUMP!"
as she rode over it.

If they saw a nice dog
they'd stop and pet it,
but if it was mean
Bartholomew would
shoo it away.

When Mrs. Pringle's sprinkler was on,
he would say, "Get ready, get set,
CHAARRRRRRGE!"

Nelly would shout "Wheeeee!"
as he pushed her through it.

When Nelly began to walk, Bartholomew
took her by the hand. "No-No!" she cried,
pulling her hand back. Nelly didn't want
any help, so Bartholomew
offered his hand only
when she really needed it.
He knew that Nelly was
getting older.

Bartholomew was
getting older, too. He
needed a walking stick
now, so they both
walked very slowly.
When they walked
up stairs, they both
held on to the railing.

The neighbors
called them "ham and
eggs" because they
were always together.
Even on Halloween they were together . . .
and on the coldest day of winter
when everyone else was inside.

One summer Bartholomew helped Nelly
learn how to skate by circling his walking
stick. "Easy does it!" he called. Then
she skated right over his foot! He wasn't
angry, though. He just whistled and
held his foot.

The first time Nelly tried to skate by herself, she fell. Bartholomew saw that she felt like crying. He pulled up something from the garden and said, "Don't be saddish, have a radish!" Nelly laughed and ate it. She didn't really like radishes, but she did like Bartholomew.

Before long, Nelly was in school
and Bartholomew had become even older.
Sometimes Bartholomew needed a helping
hand, but he didn't like to take one.
So Nelly held out her hand only when
Bartholomew really needed it.

Whenever Bartholomew had to stop
and rest, Nelly would ask for a story
about the "old days." Once after a story,
she asked him, "Will we ever run out
of things to talk about?"

"If we do," said Bartholomew,
"we just won't say anything.
Good friends can do that."

Some days they just
took it easy and
sat on the porch.
Bartholomew would
play his harmonica,
and Nelly would
make up the words.

One day Bartholomew went out alone
and fell down the stairs. An ambulance came
to take him to the hospital, and then he was
gone for a long time.

Nelly wrote him every day. She always
ended with, "Come back soon, so we can go
for walks again."

When Bartholomew came home, he was
in a wheelchair. The smile was gone from
his eyes.

"I guess our walks
are over," he said.

"No they aren't,"
said Nelly. "*I* can take
you for walks now."
She knew just how
to do it, too. Nice and
easy, not too fast.

Just before they
came to a bump, Nelly
would shout, "Get
ready for the bump!"
Bartholomew would
wave his hat like
a cowboy as he rode
over it.

If they saw a nice dog
they'd stop and pet it,
but if it was mean
Nelly would shoo
it away.

One day when the sprinkler was on,
Nelly started to go around, but she
changed her mind.

"All right, Bartholomew. Ready, set,
one, two, three. CHAARRRRRRGE!"
Nelly pushed him right through it!

"Ah ... that was fun!" said Bartholomew.

Nelly smiled. "I hope your wheelchair
won't rust."

"Fiddlesticks!" he laughed. "Who cares
if it does!"

Mrs. Pringle leaned over the fence.

"Seems just like yesterday Bartholomew was pushing you in the stroller," she said.

"That was when I was little," said Nelly. "Now it's my turn to push and Bartholomew's turn to sit . . . kind of like a trade."

Then they sat in the sun to dry. Nelly ate a carrot, and Bartholomew played his harmonica. Nelly could see the old smile was back in Bartholomew's eyes.

Thinking It Over

Comprehension Questions

1. What was the special trade?
2. How did Bartholomew help Nelly?
3. How did Nelly help Bartholomew?
4. What is a friend? Tell what you think.

Word Watch

Listed below are some words from the story. Choose one word and give some clues about it. See if someone can guess which word you are telling about.

radish	neighbor	stairs
harmonica	ambulance	carrot
porch	sprinkler	hospital

Helping a Friend

Write about a time when you were able to help a friend, or when a friend helped you.

Out Walking

by Leland B. Jacobs

When you go for a walk,
What do you see?
    A bird?
        A butterfly?
        A bee?

When you go for a walk,
What do you see?
    A bush?
        A sparkling stone?
        A tree?

When you go for a walk,
What do you see?
    A laughing child?
        A friend?
        Me?

Word Play

Some words just seem to go together. When you think of **hat,** you also think of **coat.** What do you think of when you see **red, ———, and blue?**

Read these words. See if you can finish the word twosomes and threesomes.

up, up, and ———   **hot and ———**

happily ever ———   **shoes and ———**

——— and girls   **June, July, and ———**

Something Extra

Think about some foods that go together. How many word twosomes or threesomes can you name? Here are some ideas: **ham and eggs, bread and ———.**

Growing and CHANGING

A baby can smile and cry, eat and sleep.
A two year old can walk and talk. How do
you grow and change all through your life?

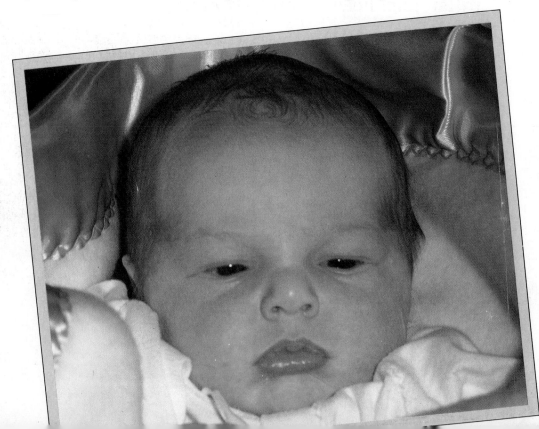

You are very special. You are a living thing. All living things grow and change. You will grow and change all through your life.

Think about how much you have already grown. How big were you when you were born? How big are you now? Think of the things you can do that you could not do as a baby. How did you learn to do them?

Now you are a child. Your body is growing all the time. Every year you get taller and heavier and stronger.

As you weigh more and become stronger, you learn to use your body well. You learn to throw and catch a ball, and to run, jump, skip, and climb.

Your mind grows along with your body. When you were very young, you learned to say words. Now you are learning to read and write those words. You are learning to work with numbers. Learning how to work and play well with others is another important way in which you are growing and changing.

When you become a teenager, you will still be growing and changing. Teenagers learn more about the world. In high school, they try to decide what kind of career they will want.

After they complete high school, some teenagers look for jobs. Other teenagers go to college. They learn things that will help prepare them for the work they want to do.

Once you become an adult, your body does not grow much more. Adults change in many other ways. Adults learn more about their careers, and they become interested in many other things.

When people get older, they may retire. This means they stop working at their careers. Then they may develop new interests and hobbies. They may travel to places that they have always wanted to see. Sometimes they even start new careers.

You have many years of growing and changing ahead of you. There are many wonderful things to learn that will make you special. What would you like to learn? What would you like to become?

Thinking It Over

Comprehension Questions

1. In what ways have you changed since you were a baby?
2. In what ways do people grow and change during their lives?

Word Watch

Give examples of what people might do during these different times in their lives:

baby   child   teenager   adult

My Life Story

Think about growing and changing all during your life. Draw a picture and write about these times.

When I was a baby, I . . .

Now that I am a child, I . . .

When I become a teenager, I will . . .

As an adult, I would like . . .

Following Directions

Listed below are some things that will help you when you follow directions. As you read each one, think why it is important.

1. Read all of the directions before you begin.

2. Get together all the materials you will need before you begin.

3. Be sure to follow the directions in the right order.

4. Look at any pictures that come with the directions.

Now read the directions for planting a seed.

Things you need:
seed   dirt   pot   water
1. Put dirt in pot.
2. Dig a small hole.
3. Put seed in hole
4. Cover seed with dirt
5. Water slowly.

Read the directions for making a play TV set. Remember the ideas that will help you when you follow directions.

Making a TV Set

You will need the following things:

tape   crayons

shoe box with
** hole cut in lid**

two new pencils

long paper

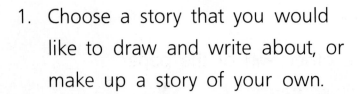

1. Choose a story that you would like to draw and write about, or make up a story of your own.

2. On the long paper, draw pictures and write sentences to tell about the story.

56

3. Ask your teacher to punch four holes in the box.

4. Put the pencils through the holes.

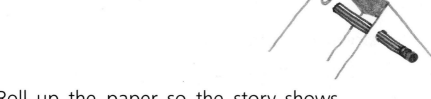

5. Roll up the paper so the story shows.

6. Tape the top end of the paper to one of the pencils.

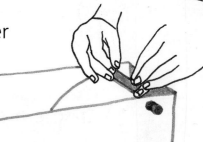

7. Tape the other end of the paper to the other pencil.

8. Tape the lid onto the box.

A DIFFERENT DAY

by Ann Miranda with María Guerrero

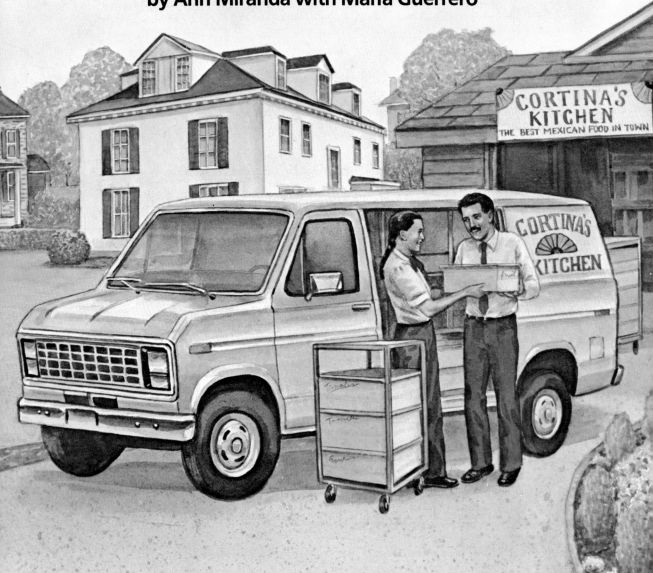

The day begins just like every other Saturday. What will happen to make this a different day?

Today is a very special day at the zoo.
It's Edgar the Elephant's birthday. Edgar
was born at the zoo twenty-five years ago.

Mr. Carr, the head of the zoo, decided it
would be fun to have a birthday party and
invite everyone who worked at the zoo.

Mr. Carr asked Mr. and Mrs. Cortina
to prepare the food for the party. They
own Cortina's Kitchen, and everyone says
Cortina's Kitchen makes the best Mexican
food in town.

Mr. and Mrs. Cortina got up early
to start preparing the food while their
children, Ruby and Ricardo, ate breakfast.
Ruby wished she could go to the zoo with
her parents, but she and Ricardo were going
bowling, just as they did every Saturday.

As Ruby was getting her bowling ball, she heard the phone ring. Mr. Cortina answered it.

"Hello, Cortina's Kitchen," Mr. Cortina said. Mr. Cortina was on the phone for only a minute, but he had a troubled look on his face.

"Carmen has a cold, and she can't help us cook today," he said.

"Oh, no!" said Mrs. Cortina. "Ann and Carlos are on vacation, and we can't fix all the food for such a big party without help!"

"We can help," said Ruby.

"Right," said Ricardo. "I don't care if I miss bowling just once. I think we really can help."

"That's great!" said Mom and Dad, almost at the same time.

"Where do we start?" asked Ruby.

"We'll have to make the tamales first," said Mom. "We're going to make three hundred of them!"

"Three hundred!" said Ricardo.

"Yes," said Mom. "That's why we really do need help. We'll have to prepare the meat filling for the tamales. And we'll need to make the corn dough for them."

Ruby and Ricardo worked all morning helping Mom and Dad fix the tamales. After lunch they put the tamales into big pots to cook.

"We have enough tamales to feed an elephant!" said Ricardo. Everyone laughed.

"I can't wait to get to the zoo," said Ruby. "I want to see the lions, tigers, kangaroos, and Edgar the Elephant."

"I'm afraid you won't be able to see the animals today," said Mom. "We need you to help with the food and to help clean up."

"Oh," said Ruby, "I forgot." Ruby looked sad. She really did want to see the animals. Ricardo looked a little sad, too.

"Someday we'll all see the zoo," said Mom.

Mom and Dad put all the food in big boxes, and Ruby and Ricardo helped put the boxes into the truck.

When the Cortinas arrived at the zoo they found the big, red and white tent that had been put up for the party. Tables and chairs had been set up inside.

Ruby and Ricardo helped place all the food on a long table in the tent. Mom put flowers and paper hats on all the small tables where people would eat.

"Everything looks beautiful!" said Ruby.

HAPPY BIRTHDAY, EDGAR

63

The zoo workers started coming into the tent, and the party began. They laughed and sang and danced — and ate tamales. It wasn't long before all three hundred tamales had been eaten.

Mr. Carr came over to talk to Mr. and Mrs. Cortina. "Thank you. Just as everyone says, Cortina's Kitchen makes the best Mexican food in town."

"We couldn't have done it without our children," said Dad. "They helped cook."

Mom smiled and hugged Ruby and Ricardo. Ricardo looked up at his mom and said, "It's too bad Edgar can't be here at his own party."

Just then Mr. Carr stood up and made an announcement. He said, "Because Edgar can't come to his birthday party, we're going to take the party to him! Come on everybody, follow me." He led the party past the lions, tigers, bears, and kangaroos.

"We are getting to see all the animals after all," Ruby said to Ricardo.

As the crowd reached Edgar, a TV truck
with the letters WHTZ pulled up. Out jumped
a man with a microphone and a woman with
a TV camera on her shoulder. The man
went to Mr. Carr and shook his hand.

"This is Paul Zepp from the TV news," Mr.
Carr announced. "Now let's all sing 'Happy
Birthday' to Edgar! Ruby and Ricardo
Cortina, from Cortina's Kitchen, will lead us!"

That night, a tired Ruby and Ricardo watched the TV news. They jumped up and hugged each other when they heard Paul Zepp say, "Now a special story from the zoo. Edgar the Elephant has turned twenty-five!"

Right there on TV, leading the others at the party in singing "Happy Birthday" to Edgar, were Ruby and Ricardo.

Ruby laughed and said, "This has been quite a day. I did get to see the animals."

"Yes," said Mr. Cortina, "I found out my children are great helpers and good cooks."

"We were on TV!" added Ricardo.

Mrs. Cortina said, "This really has been a different day!"

Thinking It Over

Comprehension Questions

1. What made this Saturday a different day?
2. What seemed to be the best part of the day for Ruby? For Ricardo? Why?

Word Watch

Some of the words below name things that belong together in some way. Tell which words go together and why.

phone	**cook**	**picture**
kitchen	**photograph**	**answer**
camera	**ring**	**food**

An Invitation

Write an invitation to Edgar's birthday party. Include the date, time, and place. You may want to mention that there will be food, music, and party hats.

MAKING PARTY HATS

1. Get crayons, glue, four big strips of paper, and three small strips of paper.

2. Decorate or color the strips.

3. Have a friend help you wrap one big strip around your head for the right size. Glue this big strip closed.

4. Lay three big strips flat as the drawing shows. Glue them at the center, then glue them to six places on the inside of your hat.

5. Lay the small strips down, and glue them at the center. Glue this to the center at the top of your hat. Try on your hat!

Nocturnal Animals

Some animals are busy at night while you are asleep. Do you know why?

When you go to sleep at night, one part of the animal world is just getting up. It is the world of nocturnal animals. Nocturnal animals are animals that are active at night.

Most nocturnal animals come out at night to look for food. The dark of the night helps keep nocturnal animals safe. Even if an enemy is near, the nocturnal animal is hard to see.

The **raccoon** is one kind of nocturnal animal. Some raccoons live on the ground, and some live in trees.

Raccoons like to eat fruit and fish. They also like to eat corn and all kinds of seeds. Because of this, farmers do not like to have raccoons in their fields.

The raccoon has dark fur with light circles on its tail. The dark circles around its eyes look like a mask.

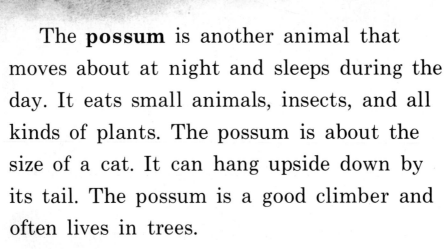

The **possum** is another animal that moves about at night and sleeps during the day. It eats small animals, insects, and all kinds of plants. The possum is about the size of a cat. It can hang upside down by its tail. The possum is a good climber and often lives in trees.

The possum has a special way of helping itself. When an enemy is near, the possum rolls over on its back and stays very still. When the possum does this, the enemy thinks the possum is dead and goes away. Do you know what "playing possum" means?

How do animals get around in the dark? People cannot see well in the dark, but many nocturnal animals can. Some nocturnal animals hear very well, too.

An **owl** uses its hearing when it hunts for food at night. When it is very dark, an owl can find and catch a mouse by listening to the mouse move through the leaves on the ground. Because owls eat small animals that like farmers' crops, these birds are sometimes called farmers' friends.

An owl cannot move its eyes as you can. An owl has to move its whole head to see something that is not right in front of it. This is not a problem because the owl can turn its head in just about a full circle.

The raccoon, possum, and owl are a few nocturnal animals. Here are two others:

Badger

Skunk

Thinking It Over

Comprehension Questions

1. What are nocturnal animals?
2. Why do they come out at night?

Word Watch

Some of the words below name things animals eat, and some name places animals live. Put the words together in the right groups.

corn   **seeds**   **trees**   **fruit**
fish   **nest**   **insects**   **ground**

Making a Chart

Make a chart telling about these animals:
Raccoon   Possum   Owl
List what they look like, what they eat, and where they live.

Animal	Looks Like	Eats	Lives
Raccoon			
Possum			
Owl	bird with feathers, eyes look large	small animals	nests in a tree

Birthdays

**written by
Ronald and
Ann Himler**

**illustrated by
Ronald Himler**

Tonight is a very special
night for Little Owl —
it's his birthday!
However, nobody seems
to have remembered,
so Little Owl decides
on a way to remind
everyone about his
birthday. Little Owl
has a good plan, but
it works out in a very
different and special way.

BIRTHDAYS

by Ronald and Ann Himler

Illustrated by Ronald Himler

Little Owl rolled over in his bed
and pulled the covers up around him. He
liked listening to the sound of the rain
falling on the leaves outside. Suddenly,
Little Owl sat up.

"Tonight is my birthday!" he cried.
He jumped out of bed and ran into the
kitchen.

"Good evening, Little Owl," Mother
said with a smile. "Are you ready for
breakfast?"

"Yes, I'm hungry," said Little Owl, sitting down at the table. "Do you know what tonight is?"

"Yes, I do," said Mrs. Owl. "Tonight is the night I must clean the cupboards."

"No, no!" said Little Owl. "I mean, do you know what *tonight* is? It's a special night."

Mother laughed. "Special? There's nothing special about cleaning cupboards."

"She forgot," Little Owl said to himself.

After breakfast, Little Owl went down the steps of the Old Tree. "She forgot that tonight is my birthday," Little Owl sighed. "This never happened before."

Little Owl walked slowly to the tall trees. He saw Raccoon sitting under a tree. "Hi, Raccoon," said Little Owl. "Do you know what tonight is?"

"Sure I do," said Raccoon.

"You do?" cried Little Owl.

"Tonight is the night my cousin promised to show me her secret fishing place," said Raccoon.

"Oh," said Little Owl, "I thought you *knew* what's special about tonight."

"I've been waiting here since sunset," Raccoon went on, "but she hasn't come yet. Well, I can't wait any longer. Listen, Little Owl. When my cousin comes by, tell her I'm down at the river. Will you do that, Little Owl?"

Then Raccoon hurried off without waiting for an answer.

Little Owl stood for a while looking down the path, but no one came.

"I'm not going to stand here all night," he thought, "not on my birthday."

Little Owl wrote a note for Raccoon's cousin and stuck it on the tree. Then he stepped back and looked at the note.

COUSIN, MEET RACCOON AT THE RIVER

"Suppose that note were a sign," he thought. "Suppose it said, 'Tonight is Little Owl's Birthday.' And suppose there were signs just like it all over the forest. Then everyone would know about my birthday!"

"That's it!" he cried. "I'll make some signs."

Little Owl ran back to his house, laughing all the way. First he found some boards, then he opened a can of paint. He stuck one wing into the paint and wrote on the first board:

"TONIGHT IS LITTLE OWL'S BIRTHDAY."

"I'll put this sign down by the river," Little Owl thought.

He painted a picture of some water at the bottom of the sign to help him remember that this sign should go near the water. He decorated each sign to help him remember where to place it.

After he had finished the signs,
Little Owl carried them down the path.
When he got to the big tree in the woods,
he remembered that he needed a hammer
and some nails. He left the pile of signs
near the bottom of the big tree and
ran home.

When he came back, all the signs were
gone. Little Owl could hear someone
hammering down in the woods, so he went
down into the woods.

Suddenly, the hammering stopped.
Mole poked his head around the stump
of a tree. "Is that you, Little Owl?"
he said in a slow, sad voice.

"Hello, Mole," said Little Owl. "I
haven't seen you in a long time."

"No one does," said Mole. "But I
saw *you,* Little Owl," he said shyly. "And
you have made me very happy."

"I have?" asked Little Owl. "You
don't look happy."

"Oh, I always look like this," sighed
Mole. "But tonight I *am* happy. Do
you know what tonight is, Little Owl?"

"I know what tonight is," cried Little Owl." "Do you know what it is?"

"Tonight is my birthday," said Mole.

"*Your* birthday?" shouted Little Owl.

"Every year it's my birthday," Mole went on proudly, "but no one ever knows. Now *you* remembered, Little Owl."

"I did?" asked Little Owl.

"Yes, you did," Mole went on. "You said to yourself that tonight must be Mole's birthday. So you made that present, Little Owl. You brought it here and set it down near my hole, then you hurried off so that I would be surprised. Oh, Little Owl," said Mole getting up slowly. "I'm so happy! Come and see."

Mole took Little Owl farther down into the woods. "Look!" he said. "My new house. Isn't it beautiful?"

Little Owl could hardly believe his eyes. Mole was building a house out of Little Owl's signs.

"I've always wanted a real house," said Mole. "And now, because of your wonderful present, I shall have one. I'll sit in it all day and look at the lovely decorations you painted for me."

Mole could not read. In fact, he could not even see very well.

"Oh, it will be a happy home for me," said Mole.

Little Owl looked at his signs. Some of them were already nailed together. "Now no one will ever know about my birthday," he sighed to himself.

Then Little Owl looked at Mole's happy face. He picked up his hammer and helped Mole build his house.

When Mole and Little Owl finished building the house, they sat together on the stump and admired the house.

"Do you know what tonight is, Mole?"
said Little Owl. "It's *my* birthday, too."

"*Your* birthday and *my* birthday are
on the same night?" cried Mole.

"That's right," said Little Owl.

"Let's go to my house and celebrate
our birthdays together," said Little Owl.

Mole was delighted. He had never
celebrated anything with anyone before.

Little Owl and Mole walked together
along the path to Little Owl's house.
Little Owl opened the door.

"Surprise!" everyone shouted. "Happy birthday, Little Owl!"

Little Owl couldn't believe his eyes.

The kitchen was all decorated with lights and colored paper. The table was set for a party, and around it stood all of Little Owl's friends.

"What's going on, Little Owl?" Mole whispered.

"A birthday party!" cried Little Owl.

He ran over to his mother and gave her a big hug. "You did remember my birthday! It's Mole's birthday, too," said Little Owl.

"Happy birthday, Mole!" said Mrs. Owl.

"Happy birthday, Mole and Little Owl!" everyone cried.

Mole and Little Owl looked at each other. Each was thinking the same thing. "A birthday is more fun when it's shared."

Thinking It Over

Comprehension Questions

1. What made this a special birthday for Little Owl?
2. What happened to the signs Little Owl made?
3. Why do you think Raccoon hurried off instead of staying to talk to Little Owl?
4. How might the night have been different if Mole hadn't found the signs?
5. Do you think Little Owl had a happy birthday? Why?

Word Watch

Interesting words were used to tell how Little Owl felt at different times in the story.

hungry   proud   surprised   special
sad   alone   happy   delighted

Tell about some times when Little Owl felt each of these ways.

Making Signs

Little Owl made signs to remind everyone about his birthday. Think of some signs you would like to make and the places you would put them. They could be for home, school, or the neighborhood where you live.

Magazine Wrap-up

Good Friends

Some of the characters named below were good friends. Which ones go together? Tell something about their friendships.

Quincy Moose   **Little Owl**   **Nelly**
Bartholomew   **Vanessa Mouse**   **Mole**

Word Watch

Here are some words from different stories.

shout   **whisper**   **whistle**
proud   **hospital** **stairs**
kitchen **sad**   **hungry**

1. Which words describe sounds?
2. Which words name places?
3. Which words tell how people feel?

A Favorite Selection

Think of all the things you have read about in Magazine One. Which selection was your favorite? Write the title of your favorite selection. Then write about why you liked it.

Books to Enjoy

Backyard Basketball Superstar by Monica Klein

The best player on the block may not get to play on the team. Her big brother is the captain, and he has to decide.

Nick Joins In by Joe Lasker

Nick comes to school in a wheelchair. He makes friends at his new school.

The Wonderful Mrs. Trumbly by Sally Wittman

Martin thinks his second grade teacher is his very best friend.

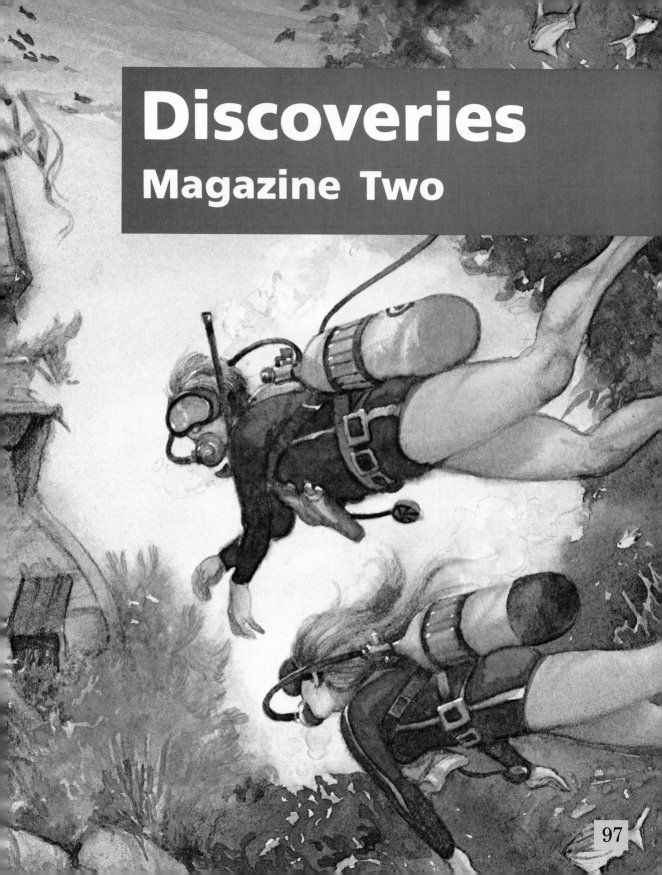

Discoveries
Magazine Two

Contents

Stories

Play

Content Selections

Poems

Skills

Vocabulary

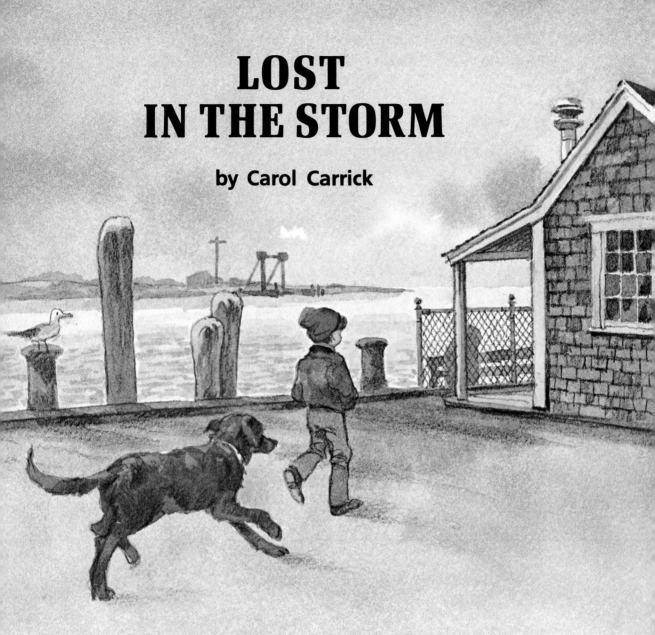

LOST IN THE STORM

by Carol Carrick

Christopher is going to play with his friend Gray on the island where Gray lives. But a storm is coming! How will the storm change things?

It was a windy day. Christopher and his dog, Bodger, waited in the ferryman's shack to keep warm.

The ferryman was inside reading his Saturday newspaper. Chris walked across the little room and looked out the window.

He could see his friend Gray waiting for him across the water.

Gray lived on an island near Chris's town. He and his mother and father were the only people who lived on the island during the winter.

"Guess you're the only one who wants to go across this afternoon," said the ferryman. He walked with Christopher along the dock to the ferry. A few seagulls were standing quietly on the dock.

"Today's no day for the beach," the ferryman said. "Even the seagulls know enough to stay in town."

"I'm going over to play with Gray this afternoon," Christopher said. Christopher had just moved from the city, and Gray was the first friend he had made in his new school.

The ferry started across the dark and choppy water.

"Wind is from the east," shouted the ferryman over the sound of the engine. "It's going to make a really high tide."

As soon as they reached the island, Gray grabbed Christopher by the arm. "Come on," Gray said. "We can play pirates before it rains."

"Okay," Christopher said. "We can bury our treasure on this island." Bodger ran off while the boys looked for things left by the tide. They filled an old basket with the treasures they found along the beach.

The clouds were getting darker when the boys heard Bodger's bark. Far down the beach they saw his reddish coat.

Christopher and Gray made a hole
in the sand with their hands and dropped
in their basket of treasures. Gray placed
an old board there to show where the
treasure was buried.

Suddenly rain was falling in big drops.
The wind blew sand in the boys' faces
as they ran laughing toward Gray's house.

Gray's father was looking out the window
for them.

"The tide's too high for the ferry to dock,"
he told Chris. "I called your mother to tell
her you would have to stay overnight."

Christopher and Gray hugged each other
and danced around.

Then, for the first time, Christopher thought about Bodger. He hadn't come home with them.

There was so much rain, Christopher could hardly see the beach. Overhead, the pounding rain was louder than the sound of Christopher's voice as he called Bodger.

Christopher wanted to go looking for Bodger, but Gray's mom and dad wouldn't let him.

"You won't be able to find each other in this storm," said Gray's father.

"He'll take care of himself," said Gray's mother.

Gray was quiet and his eyes looked troubled. Christopher knew that Gray would have gone out with him if he could. Christopher's own eyes filled with tears.

Gray's father put an arm around each
of the boys. "Since you're already wet from
the rain, why don't you get some wood and
we'll build a fire."

The boys each carried in some wood,
then Gray's mother had them go into the
bathroom to dry off and change.

Suddenly the lights went out. Everybody
gave a shout of surprise.

"The wind must have blown down a power
line," Gray's father said. "Let's do all we can
before dark in case the power is off all night."

Gray and Christopher helped gather the candles and blankets. Then Gray's mom asked them to watch the hamburgers cooking in the fireplace.

The hamburgers tasted so good, and the little house was so full of warmth and fun, Christopher almost forgot about Bodger . . . but never for very long.

The fire made their faces hot and their eyes feel heavy. Gray fell asleep on the floor, so his mother put him on the sofa and covered him without waking him up. She made a bed near the fire for Christopher by pushing two chairs together.

Christopher listened as the wind blew rain against the windows. He thought about Bodger, wet and hungry. "He doesn't know how to find me. My tracks are lost in the storm."

Several times during the night Christopher went to the window to look and listen, but there was only the storm outside.

Once he fell asleep and dreamed he had found Bodger.

Daylight came as the storm ended. Christopher woke Gray and they quietly left for the beach.

"It will be easier if we walk along the water where the sand is packed down," Gray said.

The water was high over the beach. Everything had changed. The boys couldn't even find where the treasure was buried.

Then they saw the dog tracks.

"They must be new!" shouted Gray. "Last night's tracks would be gone by now."

The tracks ran along the water for a while, then they went into the dunes. The boys stood on a high place and looked all around. Nothing moved but water and grass.

They walked along the beach. After a while the tracks came back, but there was still no dog.

"Look!" shouted Chris. Some stairs had been washed up on the beach, and under them they saw Bodger resting.

Bodger lifted his head when he heard their voices, then jumped up. The dog ran around them and back, kicking up sand. When Chris tried to grab him he pulled away, running around Christopher in circles. Then he was happily jumping all over Christopher, pushing his wet nose against Chris's neck.

When they got home, Gray's mother was
making breakfast. "The power must have
come on while we were sleeping," she said.

She patted Bodger's head. "See, I told
you he could take care of himself." Still,
she looked very pleased to see him.

When it was time to go home, Gray went down to the dock with Christopher. Seagulls were flying in the cloudless sky.

Gray rang the bell to call the ferryman over. Again, Christopher was the only one on the ferry, but he could see cars lining up on the town side to cross for a day at the beach.

"Hey," the ferryman called, "you're going the wrong way again. *Today* is beach weather."

"Bodger and I have had enough beach for now," said Christopher sleepily. "We're going home."

Thinking It Over

Comprehension Questions

1. How did the storm change things and make Christopher's visit different from the one he had probably planned?
2. Name the things in the story that helped you to know a storm was coming.

3. What happened when Christopher first got to the island?
4. What did everyone do to get ready for the storm?
5. What things do you think are different for Gray because he lives on the island instead of in town as Christopher does?

Word Watch

These words tell about where Gray lived.

grass   **beach**   **house**   **ferry**
island   **sand**   **dock**   **dunes**

Use each word in a sentence that will help someone understand what the word means.

Picture Map

Make a picture map of the island where Gray lives. Put the words from above in the right place on your picture map.

SPRING RAIN

by Marchette Chute

The storm came up so very quick
It couldn't have been quicker.
I should have brought my hat along,
I should have brought along my slicker.

My hair is wet, my feet are wet,
I couldn't be much wetter.
I fell into a river once,
But this is even better.

Reading Charts

Charts are special drawings that show information quickly. Words, pictures, or symbols that stand for something else are used on a chart. Charts may be used to help you keep track of things and organize them. Charts can show you how things go together, or are related. Some charts show the order in which something happens or the order you might follow to do something.

Writing Helps
1. Choose a story idea.
2. Write your story.
3. Revise your story.
4. Proofread your story.
5. Make a final copy.

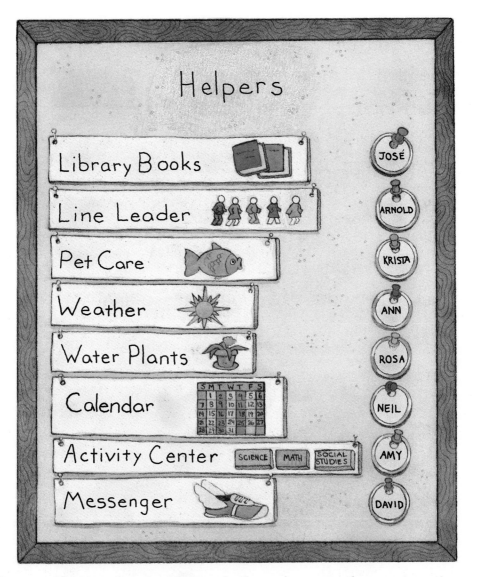

The Helpers chart helps the teacher organize the students and the classroom jobs. It also reminds the students about their jobs. Different jobs are listed. A tag with the name of a student is put next to each job.

If you were going to mix some paints together to make different colors, a color chart would be very helpful.

The color chart below shows how colors go together, or are related to each other. Red, yellow, and blue are called primary colors. They can be mixed together to make other colors. If you mix red and yellow, the chart shows that you make orange.

Color Chart

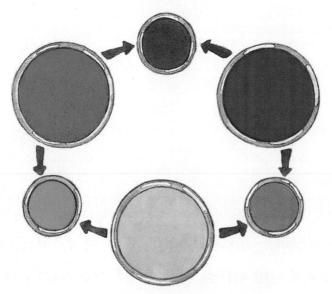

You can quickly see what happens when you mix different primary colors together.

What happens if you mix yellow and blue?

Study the chart below to learn about the water cycle.

Water Cycle

The arrow shows that tiny bits of water from lakes, seas, and other parts of the earth move up into the sky. This water becomes a cloud. The water returns to the earth as rain. The water cycle goes on all the time.

Some charts are used to show the steps you follow to do something or to solve a problem. The steps you might follow to use a computer are shown in the chart below.

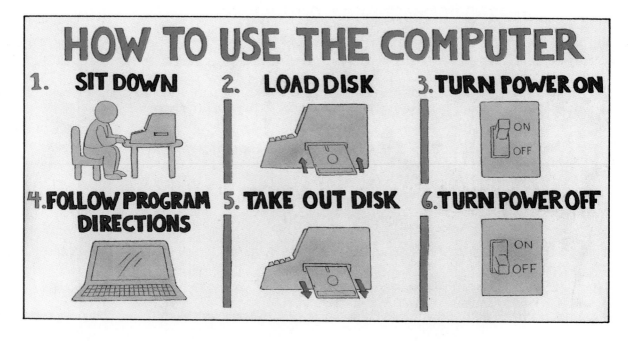

The numbers 1, 2, 3, 4, 5, and 6 tell you the order you should follow. The pictures make it easier for you to understand the words.

Charts help you to see things quickly. Charts may be found alone as a poster, or they may be found in books. They are also often seen on computers and on TV.

There are many kinds of charts. There are weather charts and charts used by business people. Charts are often used in schools to show steps to follow in working a problem, or how to do a lesson.

Skill Summary

Charts are special drawings that show information quickly. Pictures, words, and symbols are used in charts. Charts can compare things, show how things are related, and show order. Learning how to read charts will help you with many things.

What Is Weather?

Weather is all around you. It is the sun shining, rain falling, fog, and snow. Weather can be a warm breeze or a cold wind. Sun, air, and water all work together to make weather.

The sun makes the ground, lakes, and seas warmer. Tiny bits of water move into the air. These bits of water are called **water vapor.** They are so small that you cannot see them.

The air carries the vapor into the sky. As the air goes up it gets colder. Bits of water vapor stick together and turn into drops of water.

The water then becomes a **cloud**. When the drops of water in the cloud become too heavy, they cannot float in the air. Then the water falls back to the ground in drops called rain. If the air is very cold, the water comes down as snow.

Rain is very important. Rain helps plants grow, and it cleans the air. Rain gives people water for drinking and washing.

Too much rain is not good, because it can cause a **flood.** A flood is caused by water overflowing onto an area that is usually dry. Floods can damage homes and farmers' crops.

A heavy rain with strong winds is called a **rainstorm**. Wind is moving air. When the wind moves very fast, it can blow down trees and blow off parts of houses.

A heavy snow with strong winds is a **snowstorm**. The wind blows the snow. Sometimes the wind blows the snow into large drifts that make it hard to travel. Schools and workplaces sometimes close when there is a lot of snow.

A **thunderstorm** is a rainstorm with thunder and lightning. Lightning is a flash of light in the sky. Thunder is a loud noise.

A **tornado** has strong winds that move in a shape like a funnel. A tornado spins around and around, pulling things into it. A tornado can turn cars over, and pull roofs off houses and trees out of the ground.

So far, we cannot do much to change the weather, but there is a lot we can do to get ready for it.

People who tell us what the weather will be like are called **weather forecasters**. They watch the weather and study storms. Weather forecasters can usually warn people when a bad storm is coming. This gives people time to go someplace else until the storm is over. Or people may decide to stay where they are and "weather it out."

Have you ever been in a storm? What was it like?

Thinking It Over

Questions

1. What three things work together to make weather?

2. Describe these storms:

   rainstorm **thunderstorm**

   snowstorm **tornado**

3. What do weather forecasters do? How can they help people?

Activity

Keep a weather chart for a week. Make up symbols for different kinds of weather. Watch the weather and record what happens.

Sunday	Monday	Tuesday	Wednesday	Thursday	Friday	Saturday

The Princess and the Prime Minister

by Helen Kronberg Olson

Once there was a Prime Minister who had decided to rule the Kingdom after the King and Queen died. Could a young Princess win the rule of her own Kingdom?

Characters

Storyteller
Princess
Prime Minister

Dragon
Messenger
Village People

Storyteller: Once upon a time, in a tiny Kingdom by a mountain, there was a young Princess who was very unhappy. A Prime Minister who loved power had taken it upon himself to rule the Kingdom. The Prime Minister knew only one way to solve problems, and that way was to fight! The Kingdom was never quiet and happy. The Princess decided one day that she must make the Kingdom a happy place again, so the Princess went to see the Prime Minister.

Princess: I have something to tell you.

Prime Minister: *(Standing before mirror, waving his club and looking mean)* Can't you see I'm busy? Come back another day.

Princess: The time has come for me to take over the ruling of my Kingdom.

Prime Minister: What? You are too young to rule even a small Kingdom like this. Go away and don't ever speak to me of ruling again!

Storyteller: The Princess knew it did no good to argue with the Prime Minister, so she went to the Messenger.

Princess: I wish to speak to all my people. Ring the bell and call them to the castle.

Messenger: *(Running through the streets)* Hear! Hear! All gather at the castle! Hear! Hear! The Princess will speak.

People: *(Gathering at the castle balcony)* Our Princess is calling us together! This has never happened before.

Princess: *(From the balcony)* Welcome, my people.

People: Long live the Princess! Long live the Princess!

Prime Minister: *(Running out onto the balcony)* What is this? What right do you have to call the people here?

Princess: Every right! Dear people, from now on I alone will rule this Kingdom. I promise you I will do everything in my power to see there is no more fighting.

People: Hooray! Hooray!
Long live the Princess!

Prime Minister: Wait! She knows nothing about fighting or ruling a Kingdom. She is just a young Princess and she can only talk. It is better that I rule for her.

Princess: There is no problem that I could not solve as well or even better than you.

Prime Minister: Hah! You could never solve a problem as well as I.

Princess: Then let's put it to a test.

People: Yes! Yes! Put it to a test!

Princess: Yes. Whichever one of us solves the next problem for the Kingdom will be the ruler.

Prime Minister: Hah! Well, I will do it. I know that after this test the Princess must let me rule.

Storyteller: The first problem came soon enough. The Kingdom got all its water from a stream. This stream flowed down the mountainside, but now there was hardly enough water in the stream for the people to drink. The people came to ask the Princess what was to be done, and so she went again to see the Prime Minister.

Princess: Someone must climb the mountain to find out what has happened to the stream. I will go.

Prime Minister: No, I will be in charge. Messenger, climb the mountain. Find out why the stream has stopped running.

Storyteller: Late that night the Messenger returned to the castle.

Messenger: A Dragon has built his home
on the mountain. He has dug a huge hole
and blocked the stream with rocks so it
now flows into the hole to make a lake.

Prime Minister: Hah! I will teach this
Dragon a lesson he will never forget.

Princess: There is no need to teach him
a lesson. We should just ask him to
give back our stream.

Prime Minister: Don't tell me what to do!
(To the Messenger) Messenger, call the
people. Tell them to bring their clubs.

Princess: This is not the best way.

Messenger: Hear! Hear! Gather under the
castle balcony, ready to fight.

Storyteller: The Prime Minister led the people up the mountainside. No one saw the Princess following behind. She moved quickly and quietly, hiding behind rocks.

Prime Minister: *(Waving his club)* Dragon! Come out *now*!
(Dragon steps out)

People: Oh! He's huge! Watch out!

Dragon: What do you want?

Prime Minister: Open your lake so the stream can flow back down to us, or we will teach you a lesson with our clubs!

Dragon: I do not like the way you talk to
me, so I will not do what you ask.

Prime Minister: Charge him!

Dragon: Very well. If you wish to fight,
I will have to defend myself.

Storyteller: The Dragon knocked the clubs
from their hands. The people, afraid for
their lives, ran down the mountain as
fast as they could go. The Princess sat
quietly on a rock, watching and thinking.
Then she returned to the castle and went
to her workroom. She cut and sewed and
hammered. When she was finished, she
went once again to the Prime Minister.

Princess: Prime Minister, you went to see the Dragon, and now we still don't have one drop of water. You have not solved this problem, so I will try.

Prime Minister: Try if you wish, but don't ask me to save you when the Dragon catches you.

Princess: I will not ask you to save me.

Storyteller: The Princess then tossed a bag over her shoulder, and started to climb up the mountain. Many of the people called after her to come back, but she kept going.

Princess: Dragon! Dragon! I am the
Princess. I would like to meet you.

Dragon: They have sent *you* to fight me
this time?

Princess: I have not come to fight. I have
brought you a present. *(She opens the
bag, and out fall some huge red shoes.)*

Dragon: Shoes! I have never had shoes
before! *(He tries them on, then runs all
over the rocks.)* You have given me a
wonderful present. What can I give you?

Princess: Please give us back our stream.

Dragon: If that is what you want, you
shall have it. *(He goes to the stream and
tosses away the big rocks.)* Now I have
new red shoes, and you have your stream.

Princess: Thank you for being so kind.
Now I must go. But I promise you that
when your red shoes wear out, I will make
another pair for you.

Dragon: I am sorry you must leave.
I promise that if you should ever
need my help, I will answer your call.

Storyteller: Then the Princess went back down the mountain. A large crowd of people had gathered, waiting for her.

People: Hooray! Hooray! Long live the Princess! Long live the Princess!

Prime Minister: You are the winner, so now you can rule the Kingdom alone. But you must tell us, how did you make the Dragon give the stream back when all of us with clubs couldn't do it?

Princess: Using your head is better than using a club.

Storyteller: The Prime Minister said yes, but he did not really know what she meant by "using your head." Finally he decided that she must have bumped the Dragon with her head, like a goat. After that, the Prime Minister was always nice to the Princess. And under her rule, the tiny Kingdom was as happy as any Kingdom could ever be.

Comprehension Questions

1. How did the Princess win the rule of her Kingdom?
2. In what way did the Prime Minister try to solve problems?
3. Even though there are no real dragons, there are dragons in many stories. What was the dragon in this story like?
4. What did the Princess mean when she said "using your head is better than using a club"?

Word Watch

Use each of the words below in a sentence that tells about the story.

village   **balcony**   **stones**
stream   **mountain**   **castle**

Now look at the pairs of words below. In what way are the things they name alike?

balcony — porch
village — town
rock — stone
castle — house

Using Your Head

The Princess was able to win the Kingdom by using her head. Write about a time when you had a problem to solve and you solved it by using your head. What was the problem? What did you do to solve it?

The Right Meaning

Many words have more than one meaning. Which of these pictures shows a *ruler?*

If you said "both," you were right.

Look at the sentences below.

1. The Princess was the **ruler** of the Kingdom.
2. The Prime Minister used a **ruler** to measure the size of his mirror.

The word *ruler* has different meanings in these sentences. The other words in the sentence helped you know the right meaning.

Read each pair of sentences below. Find the sentence that goes with the picture.

1. There wasn't a **drop** of water in the Kingdom.
2. Please don't **drop** that bowl.

1. The **ring** just fit her finger.
2. The Messenger will **ring** the bell.

Something Extra

Feet, well, and *club* are words with more than one meaning. Make up a sentence to show one meaning. Ask a friend to make up a different sentence to show another meaning. Think of some other words with more than one meaning. Take turns making up sentences.

Nannabah's Friend

by Mary Perrine

For the first time, Nannabah must take the sheep to the canyon alone. If only she had a friend. What will Nannabah do?

Big Star was still shining through the round hole-for-smoke of their hogan roof when Nannabah's grandmother shook her very gently to wake her.

"Get up quickly, my grandchild," she said.

Nannabah sat up on her bed made from sheepskin and stretched until the sleep was out of her eyes.

Her grandmother was taking down from the hogan wall the pan for cooking their breakfast of bread-you-slap-with-your-hands. Nannabah could smell the piñon fire made outside by her grandfather.

Nannabah went outside and sat by her grandfather on his bright colored blanket. Nannabah and her grandfather sat close together in quietness.

Nannabah could hear her grandmother slapping dough in their hogan. Nannabah wanted to run to her and ask her, "My grandmother, is it today I must take your sheep to the canyon alone?" And she wanted to say, "I think you told my grandfather." But she was afraid to hear her grandmother's answer, so she stayed by the piñon fire with her grandfather.

Later Nannabah's grandmother was
kneeling by the fire cooking round thin pieces
of dough. Nannabah tried to see her eyes,
but her grandmother didn't look at her
until after they began to eat.

Then her grandmother looked at her
with gentleness, and Nannabah knew she
was going to say it. "Today, my grandchild, I
won't go with you when you take the sheep."

Nannabah wanted to hide her face with
her hands, and she tried. But her grandmother
and grandfather must have seen through her
fingers.

"Don't cry, grandchild," her grandmother
said. And her grandfather put his hand on
her shoulder with kindness.

When it was time to take the sheep
to the canyon, Nannabah's grandmother
opened the gate for the sheep. She handed
Nannabah a stick to drive them, and a can
with little rocks in it.

Nannabah hit the sheep very gently
with her grandmother's stick and started
them up the trail. She kept looking back
on her way up the mesa. From the top
of the mesa she could see her grandmother
piling wood by their hogan door.

After a while Nannabah started the sheep
down the trail on the other side of the mesa.
For a long time the sheep walked slowly
on the trail.

Then a big sheep with horns left
the trail and the others began to follow.
Nannabah ran after the big sheep with horns
and tried to stop it, but the big sheep with
horns went around her.

Soon it started up the hill and the others followed. Nannabah went in front of them and tried to push them with her foot, but she wasn't strong enough.

Then she thought of the can with little rocks in it. She took the can and shook it.

As if they had heard a snake, the sheep stopped moving. Then, slowly, they turned and walked away from Nannabah, and soon they were going down the trail again.

When they had almost come to the canyon's flat ground, the big sheep with horns started from the trail again. Two others began to follow. But Nannabah went ahead of them, and shook the can with little rocks in it, and the sheep went back.

Finally they were in the canyon. There
was a place near the canyon's end where
water fell from rocks and made a pool below.
Around the water, the grass was green.
The sheep stopped there, and began to graze,
and Nannabah sat down by them in the grass.

For a long time she watched the water
that was running down the rocks and she
listened to its sound. Then she looked up
at the sky and clouds.

She thought about her grandmother and
grandfather. And she thought about her
mother and father, and her little sister and
baby brother who were in their hogan that
was far away. She was going to hide her eyes
with her hands and cry, but she had never
cried alone before. She had never been
alone before.

Nannabah stood up and began to walk among the sheep by the water. Red mud was by the edge of the water, and Nannabah touched the mud with her fingers to feel its softness. Then, an idea came to her.

She filled her hand with red mud. Using a stick to help her fingers shape the mud, she made a doll. She named it "Little Sister."

Then she got more mud and made another doll. This doll was a baby in a cradleboard and Nannabah named it "Baby Brother."

She put Little Sister and Baby Brother on a flat rock in the sun to dry. She thought of the sheep then, and she watched them for a while. All of them were grazing in the deep grass by the water, and they were all near.

Nannabah began to make a hogan for Little Sister and Baby Brother. For the wall, she rolled red mud in her hands to make logs. She curved the logs of mud until they were round like bracelets. The roof was made from a thin piece of mud. Before she put the roof on, she made a round hole-for-smoke.

When the hogan was finished, she put Little Sister and Baby Brother on the floor inside. "It is a nice home," thought Nannabah. Then she took Little Sister and Baby Brother from the little hogan and put them on the ground outside. Nannabah was going to talk to them, but she remembered that they had no ears. And she remembered, suddenly, that she was still alone.

She looked up at Sun. Her grandmother had told her once that when it was time to start the sheep from the canyon Sun would be standing over the tallest rock. Soon Sun was there.

Nannabah put Little Sister and Baby Brother inside the little hogan. She was glad she had made them, and she was glad she had made them a home. But still she wished she could talk with them.

Then she hit the sheep gently with her grandmother's stick, and soon they were on the trail.

It wasn't long until they had come
to the top of the mesa.

From the mesa, Nannabah could see her
grandmother and grandfather near the hogan.
Her grandmother was weaving a rug on her
loom by the door. Her grandfather was
carrying corn from the wagon.

When Nannabah had come home with
the sheep, her grandmother opened the gate
again and helped her drive the sheep inside.

The next morning, when her grandmother shook her to wake her, Big Star was looking again through the round hole-for-smoke. Nannabah thought first about Little Sister and Baby Brother in the little hogan. Big Star, she thought, must be looking at them too. There was no one to wake them.

When her grandmother had made their bread-you-slap-with-your-hands, Nannabah ate with her grandmother and grandfather. Then she went to the corral. Nannabah's grandmother opened the gate for the sheep, and Nannabah started them up to the mesa.

On the other side of the mesa, tall rocks hid the canyon's floor. Nannabah looked between some of them trying to see the little hogan, but other tall rocks stood behind. Then, near the end of the trail, one rock was low. Nannabah ran ahead of the sheep and climbed up on it.

She could see the little hogan — and
something else. Sheep were grazing in the
grass by the water, and a girl was sitting
near the little hogan — a real girl.

Nannabah wanted to run ahead of her
sheep again, but she was afraid. She
wondered if the girl would smile and talk
to her and listen when she talked.

When Nannabah's sheep came to the green grass, Nannabah and the other girl looked at each other with shyness.

Nannabah sat down and took Little Sister and Baby Brother from their little hogan. She put Baby Brother in her lap, and she handed Little Sister to the other girl to hold in her lap.

The girl smiled then, and talked. "When I saw the dolls and the little hogan," she said, "I wished the person who made them would come back and be my friend."

Then Nannabah smiled and said, "I think I made little Sister and Baby Brother because I wished that you would come and be my friend."

When Sun stood over the tallest rock Nannabah and the other girl went different ways from the canyon with their sheep.

Every morning after that, when Nannabah ran ahead of her sheep and climbed onto the low rock, she saw her friend waiting by the little hogan.

Thinking It Over

Comprehension Questions

1. When Nannabah had to take the sheep to the canyon all alone for the first time, how did she feel? What did she do?
2. What happened the second time Nannabah took the sheep to the canyon alone?

Word Watch

Use the words below to tell about the area where Nannabah lived.

blanket	sheep	pool
hogan	corral	mud
piñon tree	trail	canyon

A Visit with Nannabah

Pretend that you have spent a day with Nannabah. Write a letter telling someone at home about the things you did together.

Little Puppy

From the Navajo

by **Hilda Faunce Wetherill**

Little puppy with the black spots,
Come and herd the flock with me.
We will climb the red rocks
And from the top we'll see
The tall cliffs, the straight cliffs,
The fluted cliffs,
Where the eagles live.

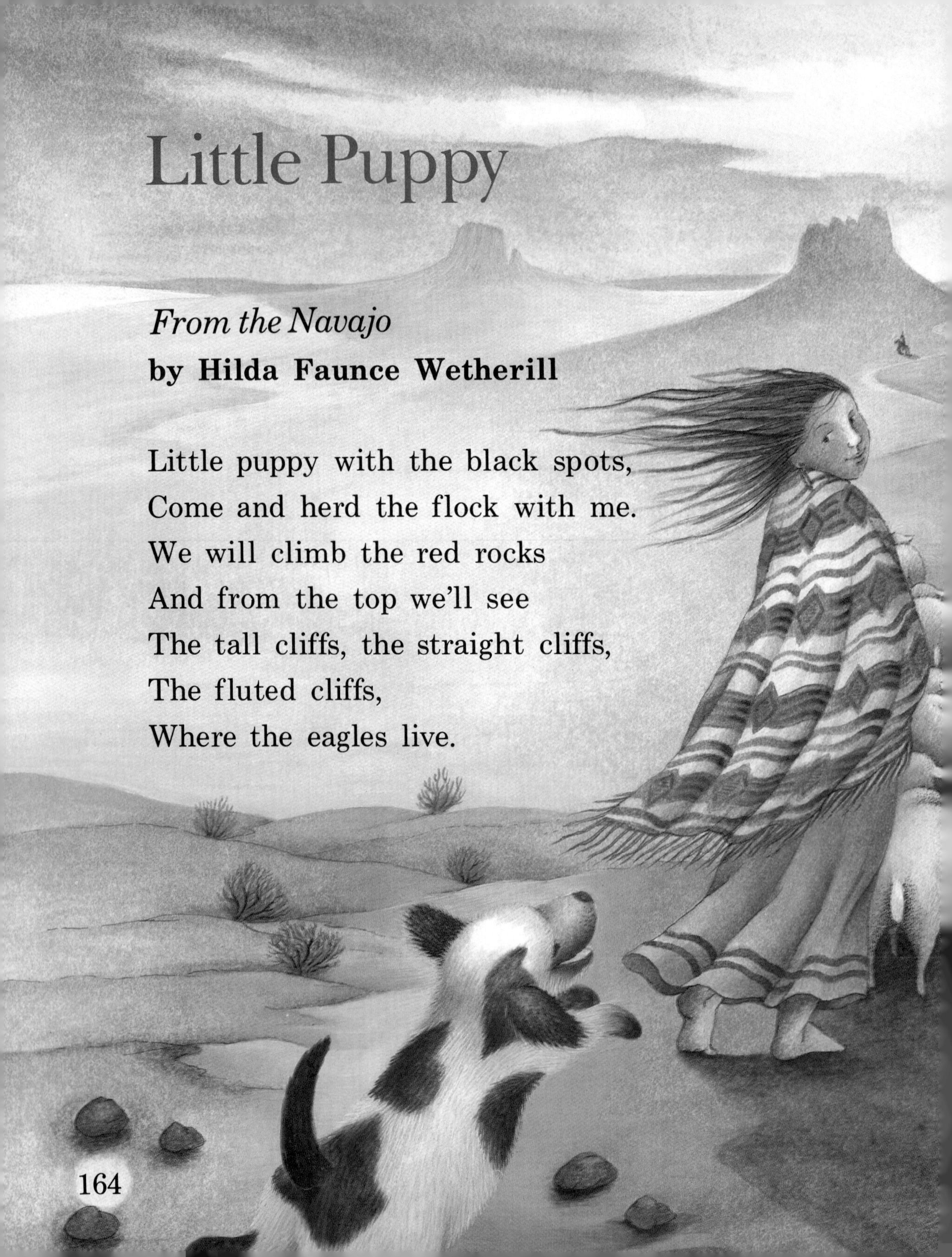

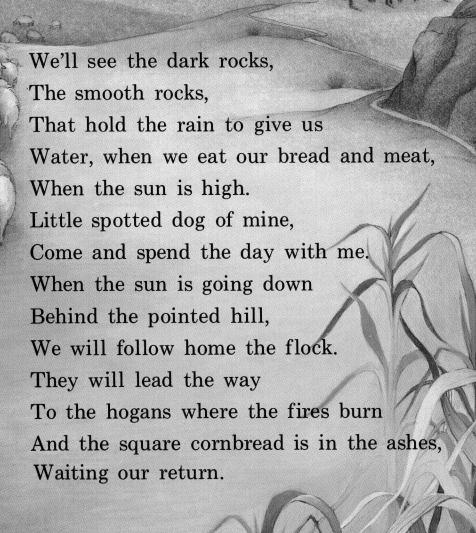

We'll see the dark rocks,
The smooth rocks,
That hold the rain to give us
Water, when we eat our bread and meat,
When the sun is high.
Little spotted dog of mine,
Come and spend the day with me.
When the sun is going down
Behind the pointed hill,
We will follow home the flock.
They will lead the way
To the hogans where the fires burn
And the square cornbread is in the ashes,
Waiting our return.

165

Noting Sequence

When you read, it is important to think about the order in which things happen. Think about the story "Nannabah's Friend."

Which picture should come first, next, and last? The answers are below.

First: Nannabah sat by the piñon fire with her grandfather.

Next: Nannabah's grandmother opened the corral gate for the sheep.

Last: The sheep went slowly up the trail.

Thinking about the order in which things happen will help you remember a story.

As you read the story below, think about what you already know and what the author says to help you remember the story.

Donna and her parents ate breakfast and then drove into the city for the big baseball game. They found their seats and soon the game started.

There were no runs until late in the game when one batter hit the ball over the fence. "A home run for our team!" Donna shouted.

The other team came to bat and a player hit the ball hard. He made it to home base, but the umpire called, "Out!"

"Hooray, our team won!" shouted Donna. Then Donna and her parents hurried to their car for the long drive home.

Think about what happened first, next, after that, and last. Are the sentences below in the right order?

1. Donna and her parents found their seats.
2. One batter hit a home run.
3. Donna and her parents hurried to their car after the game was over.
4. Donna ate breakfast with her parents.

If you think about what you already know and what the author has told you, you will decide that sentence 4 should be first. Then all of the other sentences follow in the right order. If you tell this story in the wrong order, it doesn't make sense.

Read the story below about frogs. Be ready to tell the order in which things happen.

A frog that you see sitting by a pond has not always been a frog. First there is an egg. Then the egg develops into a tadpole. The tadpole swims in the pond because it cannot leave the water. Soon the tadpole grows two back feet and then two front feet. The tadpole has become a frog. A frog can leave the water.

Can you tell how a tadpole becomes a frog? Use the correct order.

Skill Summary

Thinking about the order in which things happen will help you remember what you read. Use what you already know, and what the author tells you, to remember the order in which things happen.

One Big Wish

**written by
Jay Williams**

**illustrated by
Michael Mariano**

One day Farmer Fred
Butterspoon helps the
old woman he finds
tangled in a bramble
bush. "Good for you,
Fred Butterspoon," she
says, "and now I will
give you one wish."
One wish! What will
Fred wish for? He decides
to make *one big wish*.
What a surprise Fred
has when he gets his
one big wish!

ONE BIG WISH

by Jay Williams   Illustrated by Michael Mariano

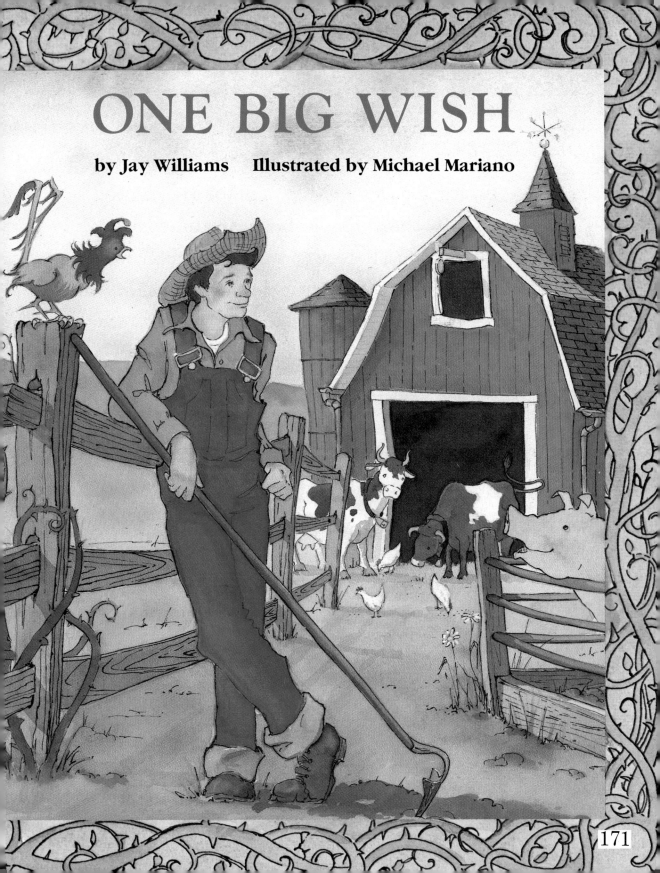

A farmer named Fred Butterspoon was working in his fields one day, when he heard a voice yelling, "Help! Help!" He ran to the bramble bush at the edge of the field. There was an old woman with her dress caught in a bramble bush.

The more she tried to get away, the more tangled she became. The more tangled she became, the louder she cried, "Help! Help!"

Fred was a kindhearted man. He took out his pocket knife and cut away the brambles. When he set the old woman free she looked at him with eyes as bright as a robin's.

"Good for you, Fred Butterspoon," said she. "And for my thanks, I give you one wish." With that, she disappeared.

One wish! Fred sighed. One wish was like trying to choose one strawberry out of a whole basket. "I guess I'd choose the biggest one," thought Fred. "So I'll take one big wish."

He thought a minute, and then he said, "I wish that all my wishes would come true."

Nothing happened. "Well, of course," said Fred. "I must try it out. What shall I wish for?" Fred sighed. "I wish I had a million dollars," he said.

174

No sooner had he said this than dollar bills began to fall down from the sky. They piled up and piled up, and Fred slipped and fell down and was almost covered with the money. He hurried out of the way and in a few seconds there was a pile of dollar bills higher than a house.

Fred danced up and down he was so happy. Then he began to wonder about what to do with all the money. He couldn't put it in his pockets or carry it under his arms.

He thought for a minute, and then he said, "I wish I had a wagon big enough to hold all this money."

At once, there was a wagon. But a wagon big enough to hold a pile of money higher than a house was a wagon so big that it would take a hundred horses to pull it!

176

"Well," said Fred, "I just wish I had a pair of horses big enough to pull that wagon."

At once, there were two horses as big as barns. "I wish them hitched to the wagon," said Fred quickly, and there they were, hitched to the wagon.

He picked up some money and threw it into the wagon. It was hard to throw, and most of it fell down to the ground. The wind blew some of it away, so he sighed, "I wish this money were all tied up in a bundle."

And so it was — one huge bundle.

"Aha!" said Fred. "I wish it were in the wagon."

And there it was, a bundle of money bigger than a house, in a wagon big enough to hold it.

Now the wagon weighed a lot. The ground couldn't hold up all that weight, and the wagon began to sink into the soft earth. When the two big horses tried to move, they sank into the mud.

Fred tried to jump into the wagon, but he was too small to reach the seat.

"I wish I were big enough to drive this wagon," he cried, and so he was.

He grabbed the reins and yelled, "Giddyap!" The horses began to pull the wagon, but it didn't move.

"Whew!" said Fred. "One of me isn't enough for this job. I wish there were six of me so I could get it done."

At once, there were five other Freds, each taller than a tree.

They all stared at each other and they all started talking at once. Since they were all Fred, they all said the same thing.

Since they were so big and their voices were so loud, they couldn't hear anything. Suddenly they all stopped talking, for they all saw that *each one* had a bundle of money bigger than a house. *Each one* had a wagon two times as big as a house, pulled by two horses as big as barns.

"GIDDYAP!" yelled all six Freds.

The big horses all stamped and tried to pull themselves out of the mud, and the big wagons sank even deeper into the mud.

When the huge horses stamped the ground, clods of mud as big as haystacks went flying through the air.

One of the wagons tipped over. The bundle of money broke, and the air was full of flying dollars.

"Whoa!" yelled all the huge Freds. "Oh, whoa! Oh — I wish everything would hold still so I could think."

And there they were, all still, the horses kicking, the wagons tipping, money and mud flying around, but everything stuck fast in the air and not moving. All the Freds were waving their arms and opening their mouths to yell, but they were all still and so were their yells.

"Oh me, oh my," sighed all the Freds, but since they could hardly open their mouths, it sounded like "O e, o i."

"I wish I'd never started this whole thing," all the Freds whispered.

Five of the Freds disappeared, so did the wagons, the horses, and the money. Fred was his own size again, and he was back at the edge of the field in front of the old woman, and the old woman was tangled in the bramble bush.

Fred was still kindhearted. He cut away the brambles with his pocket knife. The old woman said, "Good for you, Fred Butterspoon. And for my thanks, I give you one wish."

"Thank *you*," said Fred. "I wish you a very good morning."

And he put on his hat and got back to work as quickly as he could.

Thinking It Over

Comprehension Questions

1. What was the first big wish Fred made? What happened when he got his wish?
2. Do you think Fred was smart in making the wishes he did? Why or why not?
3. What was the last wish Fred made? Why do you think he made that wish?

Word Watch

horses   **barn**   **earth**
fields   **wagons**   **bramble bushes**

Draw Fred's farm. Place the words from above in the right place on your picture.

One Big Wish

If you could have one wish, what would you wish for? Suppose your wish came true. Write a short story about it.

Tongue Twisters

How fast can you say this sentence?

Farmer Fred's friends finally finished fencing five fields.

You just said a tongue twister. A tongue twister is a sentence or a group of words that are hard to say quickly. Most words in a tongue twister begin with the same sound.

Add words to make this a tongue twister.

bramble bushes become

You could say, "Bramble bushes become beautiful" or "Brown bramble bushes become bigger." What did you say? Say it quickly.

Add words to make these into tongue twisters.
1. _____ pudding pleased _____.
2. _____ goats go _____.
3. Shall she sell _____?

Magazine Wrap-up

Looking Back

The Princess, Nannabah, and Farmer Fred were three characters who all wished for something, then received the wish. What were these wishes? How did they come true?

Word Watch

The words below describe settings from different stories.

island	mesa	dock
hogan	beach	fields
ferry	canyon	barn
corral	brambles	wagon

Which words describe the setting in "Lost in the Storm"? "Nannabah's Friend"? "One Big Wish"?

Growth of a Bean Plant

Study the chart below. Then write about what happens as the bean grows.

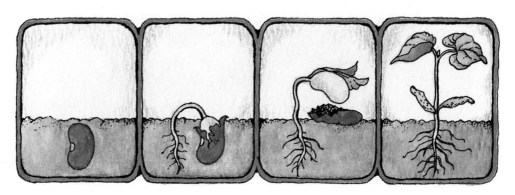

Books to Enjoy

Woodruff and the Clocks by Elizabeth Bram
This book has four short stories about a boy who likes all kinds of clocks.

The Turtle and the Monkey by Paul Galdone
Turtle works hard to get her share of the banana tree from greedy Monkey.

The Banza by Diane Wolkstein
A goat plays a banjo to scare away tigers.

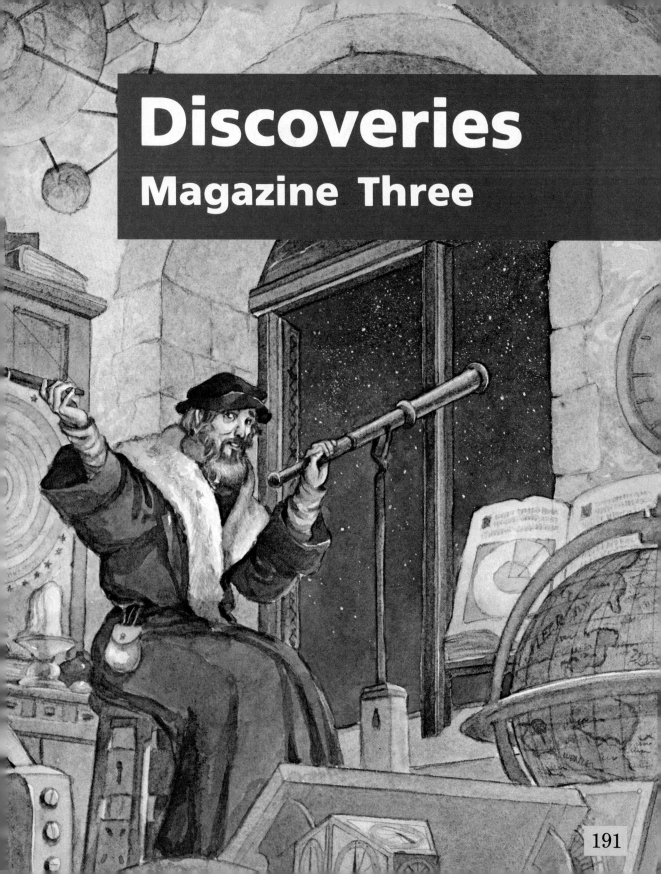

Discoveries
Magazine Three

Contents

192

Content Selections

Sumi and the Tokyo Express

by Yoshiko Uchida

Part I

Sumi lives in a small village
in Japan. She finds out
something special is
coming to her village.
What is the news?

Sumi threw off her shoes at the door and ran into the house.

"Mama!" she shouted. "Guess what has come to Mr. Oda's house."

Mr. Oda was their ninety-nine-year-old neighbor and one of Sumi's best friends.

"What is it, Sumi?" Mother asked. "Did Mr. Oda get a new front gate?"

"No, no! It's alive! It's something alive!" said Sumi.

Mother knew that Sumi couldn't wait to tell, so she said, "I can't guess."

"Mr. Oda got a new goat and she will give him fresh milk every day," Sumi said quickly. "The goat came here on a truck and her name is Miki."

"How nice for Mr. Oda," Mother said.

"I am going to take Mr. Oda's goat a welcome-to-Sugi-Village present," Sumi said, and she hurried to her room to see what she could find.

What would be a proper present for a pet goat? Sumi wondered. She looked all around her room. Finally she found an old red hat that Mother had knit for her one winter. It would be a fine present with the cold winds of winter coming soon.

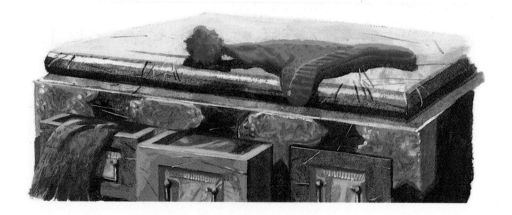

When Sumi returned to Mr. Oda's house, she found him in his yard admiring his pet.

"I brought a present for Miki," Sumi called, waving her red hat in the air. "It's to keep her head warm."

Sumi edged up to the white goat tied to the plum tree. Miki might be a fine goat, but she didn't smell very nice. Sumi reached out and put her hat on the goat's head, then backed away quickly. She wasn't at all sure that she liked Mr. Oda's new pet.

"That is a wonderful present," Mr. Oda said. "Now Miki looks like a goat with character. I'll cut some holes for her ears so the hat won't fall off. Now come inside," he said, reaching a hand toward Sumi. "Miki has a present for you, too."

Miki's present was a glass of fresh goat's milk, and it was still warm. Sumi liked milk, but she had never tasted goat's milk before. She held her breath and took a sip.

"Ugh!" she said before she could stop herself. She couldn't drink another drop, even if it *had* come from a goat with character. It would be something new to tell the class the next day, however.

Every morning just before lunch, Sumi's classmates put away their books and anyone who had special news would stand up to tell about it. Sometimes their teacher, who was also the mayor of Sugi Village, would tell about something he had read.

Mr. Mayor usually had the most interesting things to tell. After him, it was Ayako, the girl who sat in front of Sumi. Ayako's father owned the village rice shop, so he knew everything about everyone.

"Maybe today is the day I will tell some news that Ayako doesn't know," Sumi thought. She raised her hand the moment Mr. Mayor asked if anyone had some news.

"I had a drink of fresh milk yesterday," Sumi said proudly, "straight from a new goat who just came to our village. The goat is Mr. Oda's new pet," Sumi went on. "I gave her a red hat for a present."

All of Sumi's classmates laughed at the thought of a goat wearing a red hat.

Then Ayako's hand was waving. She stood up and talked in a clear voice. Her news was so exciting that everyone forgot all about Mr. Oda's goat. Ayako told about a railroad that was going to be built very near the school. It would be the first railroad to come so close to Sugi Village.

Sumi sighed and slumped back in her chair. If only Miki had been something more exciting than an old, white goat. What was a goat next to a whole railroad? "Nothing," Sumi thought, "nothing at all."

Sumi had never been on a train. Most of her classmates had never been on one, either.

"Ayako is right," Mr. Mayor said. "A railroad is coming, and the train will be an express straight from Tokyo."

Now even Sumi forgot about Mr. Oda's goat. A Tokyo Express traveling so close to the village was something wonderful. Ayako's news *was* more exciting.

As soon as she got home, Sumi told her mother about the railroad. At supper she told Father and her big brother, Taro.

Taro, who was ten and thought he knew more about everything than Sumi, seemed excited.

"If we get a railroad, maybe we'll have a station someday," he said, "and maybe the Tokyo Express will stop here!"

"Will it?" Sumi wondered.

No one knew, so Sumi said, "I will ask tomorrow."

When Sumi got to school the next day,
she asked Mr. Mayor if the express would
ever stop at their village.

Mr. Mayor shook his head. "No, it is
a high-speed express and it will stop only
at a few large cities," he explained.

"It will never stop here then?" Sumi
asked.

"I'm afraid not," Mr. Mayor answered.

"My father told me," Ayako announced,
"it will never, ever stop in Sugi Village."

Now the wait for the express began.
Soon a tunnel was dug through the mountain.
Tracks were laid across what was once a rice
field at the edge of the village. Every day
Taro and his friends watched the work on the
railroad, and sometimes Sumi went with them.

Whenever Sumi watched the work on
the tracks, she stopped at Mr. Oda's to tell
him how it was coming along. And she
always saw Miki tied to the plum tree,
looking for grass.

"If you could only do something more
exciting," Sumi would say to the goat.

And she would tell Mr. Oda, "The express
will be coming soon, but it won't stop here."

Mr. Oda always listened very carefully.
"It does seem unfriendly of it not to stop
even once," he said.

Sumi nodded. It was most unfriendly of
it to go by as though Sugi Village wasn't
even there. More and more, Sumi began to
think of the train as the Unfriendly Express.

Before long, the tracks were finished along the edge of the village. Finally one cold morning the first express came through. The whole school went out to watch the beautiful, blue train glide by.

It glided on the rails like a sled on ice, making only a *Whinnnnng* sound as it raced by. The children all shouted and waved, but the train went by without even slowing down.

Each day now the children listened for the sound of the express. First there was the *Whinnnnng* sound of the train going north. Then there was the *Whinnnnng* sound of the train traveling south.

At first the children looked out the window whenever the express went by, but after a few weeks they forgot to listen anymore. The Tokyo Express had now become just another sound of the village.

Thinking It Over

Comprehension Questions

1. What was the big news in Sugi Village?
2. How did Sumi feel about Mr. Oda's goat?
3. If someone were going to read Part 2, but had missed reading Part 1, what would you say has happened so far in the story?

Word Watch

village	**train**	**mayor**
classmates	**goat**	**sled**

1. What can glide?
2. Which are words for people?
3. Where can you find a group of people?
4. Which ones can have names?

Sugi Village

Write some sentences that describe where Sumi lives. Where is her village? What is it like?

Sumi and the Tokyo Express

by Yoshiko Uchida

Part 2

Everyone is used to the train speeding past, but this is about to change. What will the next news be about the Tokyo Express?

All night snow had fallen, and the wind had blown the snow in great drifts that leaned up against houses and trees.

Sumi and Taro tramped slowly through the snow to school.

Late that morning, when it was almost time for Mr. Mayor to ask if anyone had any interesting news, Sumi heard a strange sound. It was not the *Whinnnnng* of the express going north, but more of a soft *Whuuuuuuf* sound. Then there was a long silence. Sumi looked out the window, and saw the Tokyo Express. It was not moving one inch. It just stood still. The express had stopped at Sugi Village!

Sumi didn't even raise her hand or stand up. She just shouted, "Mr. Mayor, Mr. Mayor, the express has stopped!"

Everyone ran to the window. Sure enough, there was the blue express. In front of it, standing on the tracks, was something that looked like an animal. Was it a cow?

Sumi thought she saw a spot of red on its head. Could it be her hat? Could it be Miki way out there?

"Let's go, children," Mr. Mayor called.

Everyone ran to put on their coats and boots and hats. Then they all ran through the snow down to the train.

"Hello, Tokyo Express!" the children shouted.

"You finally stopped!" Sumi shouted.

Sumi ran to the front of the express, and she saw her old red hat. There it was, sitting on Miki's head as the goat searched for grass along the railroad tracks.

"Miki!" Sumi shouted. "Did you stop the Tokyo Express?"

Miki paid no attention to her and went right on searching for grass.

A door slid open and one of the train's conductors waved to the children.

Mr. Mayor bowed. "Welcome to Sugi Village," he called out.

The conductor bowed back and smiled. "If it weren't for the red hat, we never would have seen that silly goat," he said. "Now that we've stopped for her, we'll wait here while they clear the tracks up ahead."

The children edged up to the train and tried to look inside the windows.

"Some of the children have never been on a train," Mr. Mayor explained, "and of course, none of them have ever been on a Tokyo Express."

The conductor thought for a moment.

"Well," he said slowly, "we have only a few passengers on board, and we may never stop here again."

He waved to the children. "Come on," he called. "There's time for a quick look if you hurry."

By now all the children of the school had seen the express stop, and they came running out to see it. Taro and his classmates were soon climbing on board, too.

Sumi had never seen anything so new and beautiful. The windows were wide. The chairs were roomy and leaned back so you could sleep in them. There were little tables that folded up into the armrests.

The conductor led them through the passenger cars and into the dining car. The wonderful smells made Sumi's mouth water. The train was like another world. Sumi took a deep breath in order to keep part of it inside of her for a while.

The conductor looked at his watch. "All right, children," he said. "Time for everyone to get off. We'll be leaving soon and we can't take you with us. Did someone move that goat from the tracks?"

The children hurried off the train and Sumi ran to get Miki.

"Come on, Miki," she said. "You really did something exciting today, you did!"

Sumi could hear a voice on the train's loudspeaker announcing that the express would soon be under way. Then the door slid shut, and the express train began to glide to the north.

"Good-by, Sugi Village!" the conductor called.

"Good-by, Tokyo Express!" the children shouted.

"Thank you," Mr. Mayor added, waving his hat.

And then it was gone.

"It will never stop again," Sumi said sadly.

"But it stopped once," Mr. Mayor said, "and that is something."

Sumi nodded. It was true. And Miki was the one who had done it.

"*Hooray* for Miki!" Taro shouted.

Everyone gathered around and wanted
to touch Miki's shaggy sides ... even Ayako
came close. Ayako told Sumi that as soon
as she got home, she was going to tell her
father about Miki so he could tell everyone
in the village how the goat had stopped the
Tokyo Express.

Somehow her classmates seemed to think that Sumi was special, too, because she was Miki's friend. She was excused from class so she could take Miki back to Mr. Oda. It was a great honor, Sumi thought.

She led Miki carefully down the snowy paths to Mr. Oda's yard and tied her to the plum tree. Now that Miki was such a famous goat, she must not run away again.

Sumi hurried inside. She could hardly wait to tell Mr. Oda what had happened.

"Miki stopped the Tokyo Express!" she shouted in her loudest voice.

Mr. Oda, who was sleeping, woke up with a start. "What? What?" he asked.

Still shouting because she couldn't stop, Sumi told him how Miki had stopped the Tokyo Express and how they had all been invited on board to see what it was like inside.

"Ah, ah," Mr. Oda said, "and what was it like, this Tokyo Express?"

"It was new and beautiful and clean," Sumi said, closing her eyes so she could remember. "It was as warm as springtime, and it even had a wonderful smell."

"I see," Mr. Oda said. "I see. We must go tell Miki what a fine thing she did."

"It's cold outside," Sumi warned, "and the snow is deep."

But Mr. Oda didn't care. "What is a little snow on such a day?" Mr. Oda put on his coat, and went out holding Sumi's hand.

Miki stood calmly beside her plum tree, looking as though she had been standing there all day.

"Well, well, Miki," Mr. Oda said, reaching out to pat her head. "You are quite a special goat now. Sugi Village will long remember you for stopping the Tokyo Express."

Miki went right on eating, and Sumi no longer wanted her to be anything different. After all, Miki had done something today that no one else in all of Sugi Village could do. And that was more than you could say about any goat.

Sumi edged up close to Miki's ear. "You are a wonderful goat, Miki," she whispered.

Miki stopped grazing and looked up at Sumi's face. Sumi smiled and patted her gently on the head. She knew that Miki had listened, and she was sure that this time she understood.

Thinking It Over

Comprehension Questions

1. What was the latest news about the Tokyo Express?
2. Why did Sumi's present to Miki turn out to be a special present?
3. What was the Tokyo Express like inside?
4. How does Sumi feel about Miki now? Why?
5. Do you think the Tokyo Express will ever stop in Sugi Village again? Why or why not?

Word Watch

These words are used in "Sumi and the Tokyo Express" in place of the word *said*.

asked	**wondered**	**sighed**
shouted	**explained**	**announced**
called	**warned**	**whispered**

Find some places in either Part 1 or Part 2 where you could use these words in place of the word *said*.

Write a Report for Mr. Mayor.

Pretend you are one of Sumi's classmates. Mr. Mayor has given you this job. Write a report telling about the Tokyo Express stopping in Sugi Village.

LIVING PLACES

by Dorothy Rickards

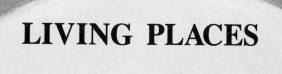

Where do you live?

The whole world over
People live in different places —
Up on a mountain, down by a river,
In crowded cities, or open spaces,
In houses, in flats, in tents, or trailers,
Underground, on the ground,
   high in the air,
Where it's hot, where it's cold,
Where it's dry or raining,

Millions of people everywhere.

Using Context

Many words have more than one meaning. If you are not sure of the meaning of a word, the meaning of the other words in the sentence will often give you a clue. Using the meaning of the other words to help with the meaning of an unknown word is called **using the context.**

Read the sentence below and think what the other words tell you about *drew.*

We **drew** pictures with our colored markers.

The meaning of the other words in this sentence tells you *drew* means "made a picture." The words *colored markers* and *pictures* were clues for the meaning of *drew.* The context in the sentence helped you with the meaning.

You can use the context in a sentence to learn a new meaning for a word. You may or may not know the meaning for *drew* in the sentence below. Use the context to help you with the meaning.

The boat **drew** near the dock.

In this sentence, the word *drew* does not mean "made a picture." The other words in the sentence helped you to learn a different meaning for *drew*. The words *boat, near,* and *dock* are clues. The context tells you that in this sentence *drew* means "moved toward."

Below is another sentence using the word *drew*. The meaning of the word *drew* in this sentence may be new to you. Use the context to help you with the meaning for *drew*.

We **drew** our drinking water from the well at the farm.

In this sentence, the context helped you decide *drew* does not mean "made a picture" or "moved toward." *Drinking water* and *well* helped you with the meaning for *drew*. The context tells you that *drew* here means "pulled up."

As you read, remember to use the context to choose the right meaning or to learn new meanings for words.

In each sentence below, use the context to get the right meaning for each word in heavy black letters.

1. Ted drove over a nail, and now his car has a **flat** tire.
2. Please put the roses on the plant **stand.**
3. The bear's **coat** was shaggy after the long winter.
4. The truck slid off the wet road onto the **shoulder.**
5. She works in a **plant** that makes cars.

Skill Summary

- Using the meanings of other words to help with the meaning of an unknown word is called using the context.
- You can use the context to choose the right meaning for a word when you know the word has more than one meaning.
- You can also use context to help learn a new meaning for a word.

SEND WENDELL

by Genevieve Gray

Wendell's older brother and sister always
say "Send Wendell" when there is a job
to be done. What will change this?

Wendell lived in an apartment with Mother, Father, William, Alice, and the baby, Anthony. Everybody was happy — most of the time — but there was always work to do.

One day, Mother said, "William, please go down and see if there is any mail."

"I have to do my homework now," said William. "Send Wendell."

So Wendell went down to the mailboxes in the front hall. He found a letter in their mailbox and hurried back to give it to Mother. She read the letter and smiled.

"My brother, your Uncle Robert, is coming to see us!" she said. "He's coming all the way from California on his trip, and he'll be here in a few days."

Wendell knew about Uncle Robert. He had a farm in California. California was far away and Wendell had never seen him.

The days went by, and the family got ready for Uncle Robert's visit. Wendell did more to get ready than anyone else, except Mother and Father.

"Alice," said Mother, "please take the baby for a walk while we clean the apartment."

"I have to finish making this dress," said Alice. "Send Wendell."

Later Father said, "William, please go and get my good suit at the cleaner's."

"I just got home from school," said William. "Send Wendell."

Father gave Wendell money to pay the cleaning bill, and Wendell started downstairs.

When Wendell got to the first floor he saw the tallest man he had ever seen. The man was reading names on mailboxes.

Wendell stopped and stared up at the man, and the man turned and stared down at Wendell.

Then the tall man began to smile the same way Mother smiled. "You must be William," he said.

"No, I'm Wendell."

"I'm your Uncle Robert," said the man.

All of a sudden, Wendell began to feel nice inside. He smiled a big smile and said, "I'm going to the cleaner's. I have to pick up my father's suit."

"You're a good boy to help out like that," said Uncle Robert. "Why don't I walk to the cleaner's with you?"

As they walked down the street, Uncle Robert asked, "You never saw your grandfather, did you?"

"No," said Wendell.

"When you grow up, I'm certain you're going to look like him," said Uncle Robert.

Wendell smiled proudly.

On the way back from the cleaner's, Uncle Robert asked about the family. Wendell told him a little bit about everybody, but most of the time he just smiled happily.

When Wendell and Uncle Robert got home,
everyone started talking at once. William
and Alice jumped up and down and the baby
gurgled. Mother was so glad to see her
brother, she gave him a big hug. Father
shook his hand and patted him on the back.

That night dinner was special. Everybody
ate and listened hard to what Uncle Robert
was saying.

Saturday they all went to the zoo together. On Sunday, they had a picnic in the park. Monday night, Uncle Robert took the whole family to the movies.

In between times, Uncle Robert told Mother and Father about his farm in California. His own children were growing up, he said, and they all wanted to go to work in the city.

All too soon it was time for Uncle Robert to go back to California.

"Wendell," Uncle Robert said, "your mother and father say that when you grow up a little more, you can come to visit me on the farm. Would it suit you to come to California?"

"Yes," said Wendell. He held tight to Uncle Robert's hand.

The morning after Uncle Robert left, Mother was busy cleaning the apartment.

"Alice," said Mother, "Mrs. Wilson let us have this big pan to use while Uncle Robert was here. Take it back to her, please."

"I have to phone my friend Julie about getting my hair cut," said Alice. "Send Wendell."

Wendell smiled. "I have to write a letter to Uncle Robert," he said.

So Alice had to go anyway.

Thinking It Over

Comprehension Questions

1. What changed so that Wendell's older brother and sister no longer said "Send Wendell" when there was a job to be done?

2. How was Wendell different from Alice and William?

3. What made Uncle Robert's visit a special time for the family?

4. What do you think Wendell wrote in his letter to Uncle Robert?

5. Why do you think Uncle Robert invited Wendell to visit him in California?

Word Watch

Each word below has more than one meaning. Can you think of two meanings for each word? Use the word in a sentence to show one meaning, then use the same word in another sentence to show a different meaning.

finish   suit   letter   pick   bill   hard

Here is an example:
Ann wiped the table until the **finish** shined.
Kate was first to **finish** the race.

My Job

Wendell did many jobs to help his family. Are there things you do to help your family? Write about them.

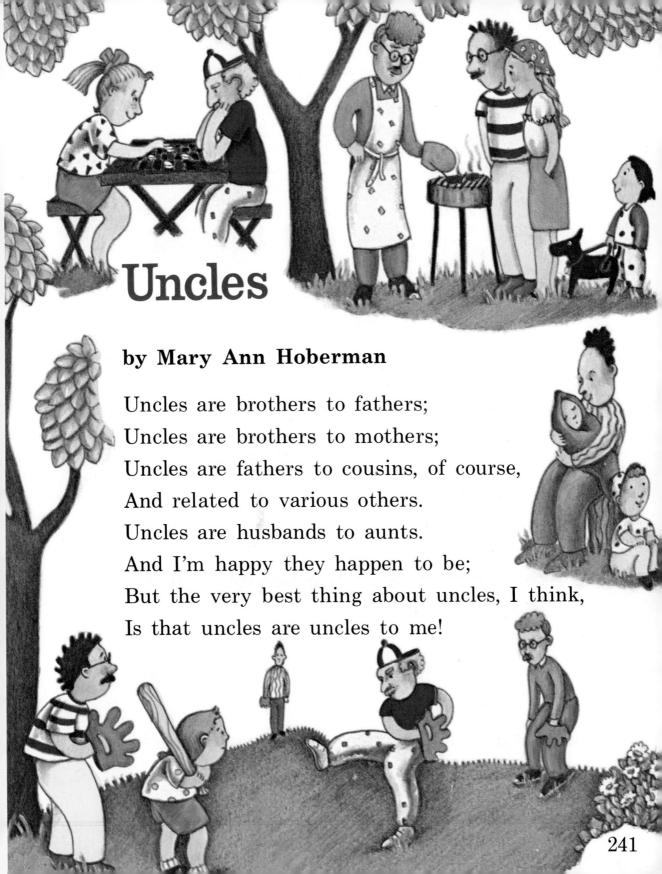

Uncles

by Mary Ann Hoberman

Uncles are brothers to fathers;
Uncles are brothers to mothers;
Uncles are fathers to cousins, of course,
And related to various others.
Uncles are husbands to aunts.
And I'm happy they happen to be;
But the very best thing about uncles, I think,
Is that uncles are uncles to me!

241

THE GIANT
WHO THREW
TANTRUMS

by David L. Harrison

Only a little boy knows that a giant lives
on Mount Thistle and that this giant is
throwing tantrums. Can the little boy help
the giant?

At the foot of Mount Thistle lay
a village. In the village lived a little boy
who liked to go walking.

One Saturday afternoon the little boy
was walking in the woods when he heard
a terrible noise. He popped behind a bush.
Before long a huge giant came stamping
down the path. He looked upset.

"Tanglebangled — ringlepox!" the giant
yelled. Then he began hitting his head
against a tree until the leaves shook off
like snowflakes.

"Franglewhangled — whippersnack!" the giant roared. Pulling up the tree, he whirled it around his head and knocked down twenty-one other trees. Talking to himself, he stormed up the path toward the top of Mount Thistle.

The little boy hurried home. "I just saw a giant throwing a tantrum!" he told everyone in the village. They only smiled.

"There's no such thing as a giant," the mayor told him.

"He knocked down twenty-one trees," said the little boy.

"Must have been a tornado," the weather forecaster said with a nod. "Happens around here all the time."

The next Saturday afternoon the little boy again went walking. Before long he heard a terrible noise. Quickly he jumped behind a tree.

Soon the same giant came storming down the path. He still looked upset.

"Pollywogging — frizzlesnatch!" he yelled. Throwing himself down, he pounded the ground with both fists. Rocks bounced like popcorn.

Looking very mean and angry, the giant puckered his lips into an "O."

He drew in his breath sharply. It
sounded like somebody slurping soup.

"Phooey!" he cried.

Grabbing his left foot with both hands,
the giant hopped on his right foot up the
path toward the top of Mount Thistle.

The little boy hurried home. "That giant's
at it again," he told everyone. "He has
a terrible temper and he threw a tantrum
that made the ground shake!"

"Must have been an earthquake," the police chief said. "Happens around here sometimes."

The next Saturday afternoon the little boy again went walking. Before long he heard a frightening noise, so he jumped behind a big rock.

Soon the giant came storming down the path. When he reached the little boy's rock, he puckered his lips into an "O." He drew his breath in sharply with a loud, slurping sound.

"Phooey!" he cried. "I *never* get it right!"

The giant held his breath until his face turned blue and his eyes rolled up.

"Fozzlehumper — backawacket!" he shouted. Then he stormed up the path toward the top of Mount Thistle.

The little boy followed him. Up and up he climbed to the very top of Mount Thistle.

There he found the giant's home. The giant was sitting outside crying.

"All I want is to whistle," the giant sighed through his tears, "but every time I try, it comes out wrong!"

The little boy had just learned how to whistle. He knew how hard it could be, so he walked over to the giant.

The giant looked surprised. "How did *you* get here?"

"I know what you're doing wrong," the little boy said.

When the giant heard that, he leaned down and put his hands on his knees.

"Tell me at once!" he begged.

"You have to stop throwing tantrums," the little boy told him.

"I promise!" said the giant, who didn't want anyone thinking he had poor manners.

"Pucker your lips ... " the little boy said.

"I always do!" the giant said.

"Then blow," the little boy added.

"Blow?" asked the giant.

"Blow," said the little boy.

The giant looked as if he didn't believe it. He puckered his lips into an "O." He blew. Out came a long, low whistle. It sounded like the whistle of a train. The giant smiled, then he shouted, "I whistled! Did you hear that? I whistled!" Taking the little boy's hand, he danced in a circle.

"You're a good friend," the giant said.

"Thank you," said the little boy.

"Sometime maybe we can whistle together, but right now I have to go. It's time for my dinner."

The giant sat in front of his home
and waved good-by.

The little boy hardly ever saw the giant
after that. But the giant kept his promise
about not throwing tantrums.

"We never have earthquakes anymore,"
the mayor liked to say.

"Haven't had a tornado in a long time,"
the weather forecaster would add.

Now and then they heard a long, low
whistle somewhere in the distance.

"Must be a train," the police chief
would say.

But the little boy knew his friend
the giant was walking up the path toward
the top of Mount Thistle — whistling.

Thinking It Over

Comprehension Questions

1. How was the little boy able to help?
2. What kinds of things did the giant do when he threw tantrums?
3. What was the real reason there were no longer "earthquakes" and "tornados" in the village?

Word Watch

Use each action word in a sentence.

roared	**bounced**	**slurped**
whirled	**puckered**	**begged**

Learning Something New

The giant wanted very much to learn how to whistle, and the little boy helped him. Write about a time when you helped someone learn something new.

WHISTLING

by Jack Prelutsky

Oh, I can laugh and I can sing
and I can scream and shout,
but when I try to whistle,
the whistle won't come out.

I shape my lips the proper way,
I make them small and round,
but when I blow, just air comes out,
there is no whistling sound.

But I'll keep trying very hard
to whistle loud and clear,
and someday soon I'll whistle tunes
for everyone to hear.

Alphabetical Order

round	team

Often when many words are listed together, they are listed in alphabetical order. This helps you to find words quickly.

Suppose you are looking for the word *team* in an alphabetical list. Will you look for *team* at the beginning of the list, or near the end of the list? Near the end of the list is right. If you see *round*, will you look for *team* before or after *round*?

You might think, "*Round* begins with *r* … *r, s, t. Team* begins with *t* … *t* comes after *r* in the alphabet. I need to keep going to find *team.*"

You thought about the first letter of *team* and the first letter of *round*, and you also thought about the alphabetical order for these two letters.

team	thousand

Let's suppose again that you are looking for the word *team*, but this time the first word you see is *thousand*. Does *team* come before or after *thousand*? How do you know?

You might decide that *team* comes before *thousand* by thinking something like this: "I see the word *thousand*. I want the word *team*. Both *team* and *thousand* begin with *t*. When two words begin with the same letter, I need to look at the second letter in each word. The second letter of *team* is *e*. The second letter of *thousand* is *h* … *e, f, g, h. E* comes before *h. Team* comes before *thousand*. I need to look for *team* before the word *thousand*."

A B C D E F G H I J K L M N

O P Q R S T U V W X Y Z

team		tent

Often you will find words that begin with the same two letters. Which word comes first?

You need to look at the third letter. If again you are looking for the word *team,* and the first word you see is *tent,* you might think this way: "The first two letters of *team* and *tent* are the·same . . . *te.* The third letter in *team* is *a* and the third letter in *tent* is *n.* The letter *a* comes before the letter *n* in alphabetical order, so *team* comes before tent.

Look at the words below. Decide which word in each pair comes first in alphabetical order. Be ready to tell how you decided.

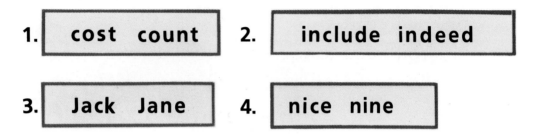

1. **cost count**

2. **include indeed**

3. **Jack Jane**

4. **nice nine**

When you couldn't use the first or second letter, you used the third letter. *Cost* comes before *count*. *Include* comes before *indeed*. *Jack* comes before *Jane*. *Nice* comes before *nine*.

Skill Summary

When you are deciding the right alphabetical order, remember –

● When you have two words that begin with the same letter, look at the second letter.

● When you have words that begin with the same two letters, look at the third letter.

IT'S NOT
FAIR!

by Elaine Knox-Wagner

Susan thinks it's not fair being the
oldest child in the family. Will she
find out that she's right?

Ever since I was born, I've been the oldest kid. It's not fair. Being oldest means I got to our house first. It means my room and toys and Dad and Mom were all mine — until my brother came. Then I had to share ... EVERYTHING.

Being oldest means I have to set a good
example. When I want another ride on the
merry-go-round and my folks say we have
to go, I climb off my favorite horse right
away. My brother yells and holds onto his
horse's neck. My father just smiles and
lifts him off the horse.

Being oldest means I should
... mind the teacher
... and get A's
... and be an engineer like my dad
... and make my bed without wrinkles
... and say "Thank you" and "Please"
... and never do ANYTHING wrong.
It's not fair.

In the summer, we have picnics at my Grandma and Grandpa Wentworth's. The children eat first, but only ten fit at the picnic table. Guess who's the oldest cousin? Guess who makes eleven? Guess who waits to eat?

At Sunday's picnic, I got angry. There I am, starving.

"I want a place on the bench," I tell my grandma.

"You can eat with the grown-ups," she says.

"I want to eat *now*," I say. "I can't wait."

"Oh, Susan," says my dad, while he's feeding my brother, "Why don't you go and talk to your grandpa for a bit?" I grab a carrot so I won't starve.

Grandpa is working on his car. It's very old and shiny black. Grandma says it has first place in his heart. She means that he really likes it.

"I don't like being the oldest kid," I tell him. "It's not fair." He nods and hands me a screwdriver.

"I can't even eat with the other kids," I say. "There's no room for me." He nods again and hands me a wrench.

"I'm a kid, too," I say.

"Mmmm," he says. "Would you aim this flashlight right over there?" I put the screwdriver in my hat, then aim the light so he can see.

"Just as I thought," he says. "Wrench?" I hand him the wrench.

"Screwdriver?" He takes it from my hat, and puts the wrench around a bolt. He tries to use the screwdriver with his other hand.

"By jiminy," he says, "I can't do both at once."

"I can help," I say. He nods. "Okay. You hold this wrench. Don't let it slip." Grandpa turns the screwdriver. I use both hands and all my strength to hold the wrench still.

Just when I think I can't hold it any longer, Grandpa says, "That's it, Pal, we did it." We close the hood carefully, and put our tools back where they belong. Then we wipe our hands on rags.

"Hey, Marge," Grandpa calls to my grandma. "We're going out for a spin. We've got to roadtest this repair job."

All the cousins who can walk and talk jump up from the table.

They run toward us.

"Me, too! Me, too!" they yell.

"Not this time," Grandpa says. "Not this time." He backs the car slowly down the driveway, and the cousins run after us.

"Just because you're oldest, you get to do EVERYTHING," one cousin yells.

"Finish eating," says Grandpa. "You'll have your turn later."

As we drive, Grandpa listens to the engine, and I keep quiet so he can hear. We drive around the lake and through downtown and out to the highway.

"It runs like a top," he says finally. "We did a good job on it, Pal." He lets me turn on the radio as we head back to the house.

Ever since I was born, I've been the oldest kid. Most of the time it doesn't feel fair, but sometimes it does feel fair.

Thinking It Over

Comprehension Questions

1. What helped Susan change her mind?
2. How did Susan help Grandpa? How did Grandpa help Susan?

Word Watch

starving   **radio**   **repair**   **screwdriver**
wrench   **hood**   **rags**   **flashlight**

1. Which words name *tools*?
2. Which word means *to fix*?
3. Which word means *very hungry*?
4. Which word means *pieces of cloth*?
5. Which words name *parts of a car*?

Talking to Susan

Write what you would tell Susan about being the oldest child, or the youngest child, or a middle child, or an only child.

A Better Word

An author can choose from many words with almost the same meaning. Sometimes when an author uses one word instead of another the meaning becomes clearer. Read the two sentences below.

1. They **walked** through the deep snow.
2. They **tramped** through the deep snow.

The words in heavy black letters mean about the same thing – but not quite. *Tramped* is a better word in this sentence, because it makes the meaning clearer.

Read these sentences. Then answer the questions.

1. Father **raced** out to the car.
2. Father **ran** out to the car.

In both sentences Father went to the car in a hurry. In which sentence did Father seem to go faster? Why?

1. The rain **fell** against the window.
2. The rain **pounded** against the window.

In both sentences it was raining. In which sentence did it seem to rain harder?

Read each sentence below. Choose the word that makes the meaning clearer.

1. Lightning (**was/flashed**) in the sky.
2. The wind (**came/blew**) suddenly.
3. A tree (**moved/shook**) in the wind.
4. The tree (**dropped/crashed**) to the ground.

Communities – Large and Small

What is a community? A **community** is a place where people live and work. A community provides people with places to buy the things they need. It also provides services such as schools, libraries, and police and fire departments.

A **city** is a large community. It is made up of many people and many neighborhoods. A city is often called an **urban area**.

A **town** is a small community. A town and the countryside around it make up a **rural area**.

In a city, houses are often close together. A city family might live in an apartment building. This is a large building in which each family has a set of rooms to use as a home.

In urban areas, homes, schools, and stores are close together, so people who live in cities do not have to go far to get things they need.

What do people in apartment buildings see from their windows?

In rural areas, the homes are far apart. There is a lot of land but there are few people. It is often some distance from one house to another.

How do people in rural areas get the things they need? Some people on farms grow or make some of the things they need. They go to the nearest town or city to get other things.

What do people in rural areas see from their windows? What sounds do they hear?

Urban areas often have theaters where people can go to watch a play. In urban areas, there are also different kinds of museums. A museum is a place where people can go to look at things that will help them learn about art, history, or science. Many cities have street fairs where people can play games and buy things.

Farmers can buy and sell things at a country fair. Rodeos and country fairs may be a part of living in a rural area.

Which of these pictures show what you
might see in an urban area? Which show
what you might see in a rural area? Are
there things you might see in both areas?

There are many kinds of communities.
Each is special in its own way. What is
your community like? What makes it special
to you?

Thinking It Over

Questions

1. How would you explain what a community is?
2. What does a community provide for the people who live in it?
3. Name some ways in which urban and rural areas are different from each other.

Activity

Suppose some people wanted to come and visit your community who had never been there before. What could you tell them about your community? Where could they go? What would they see?

Magazine Wrap-up

Children in a Family

You know what Susan felt about being oldest in her family from reading "It's Not Fair." How did Wendell feel about his place in his family in "Send Wendell"? What happened in each story to change things?

Word Watch

The words below have more than one meaning. Use each word in a sentence to show one meaning. Then use it in another sentence to show a different meaning.

train   drew   plant   suit   sink

Your Favorite Character

Think of the characters you have read about in this book. The Table of Contents will remind you of the stories. List your three favorite characters. Write about why you chose each one as a favorite.

Books to Enjoy

Tye May and the Magic Brush
by Molly Garrett Bang

This Chinese fairy tale tells about a girl and her magic paintbrush.

Just Us Women by Jeannette Caines

A little girl and her aunt have fun on a long car trip from New York to North Carolina.

Willie Blows a Mean Horn by Ianthe Thomas

A small boy wishes he could play the trumpet the way his father does.

Daniel's Duck

**written by
Clyde Robert Bulla**

**illustrated by
Nancy Edwards Calder**

Daniel, Jeff, Mother,
and Father live in a log
cabin on a mountain.
During long, cold winter
nights they make things
for the spring fair.
Father is making some
moccasins, and mother
is making a quilt. Jeff
will carve a box, but he
doesn't think Daniel can
carve anything. Daniel
wants to carve a duck.

Daniel's Duck

Clyde Robert Bulla

Illustrated by Nancy Edwards Calder

Jeff and Daniel were brothers. They lived in a cabin on a mountain in Tennessee. Jeff had a good knife, and he could carve things out of wood. Jeff carved a wooden dish. Later he carved a spoon to go with the dish.

"Some day," Jeff said, "I want to carve an animal like Henry Pettigrew's."

Henry Pettigrew lived in the valley, and although Jeff and Daniel had never met him, they had seen his work. He was a woodcarver. Some people said he was the best woodcarver in Tennessee because all of his animals looked real. His birds looked as if they could fly, and his horses looked as if they could run.

"Even though animals are hard to carve," said Jeff, "I want to make one like Henry Pettigrew's sometime."

"I want to carve an animal, too," said Daniel.

"You're not old enough," Jeff said.

"Yes, I am," said Daniel. "I could carve an animal if I had a good knife and some wood."

"It takes more than that," said Jeff.

"What does it take?" asked Daniel.

"You really have to know how," said Jeff. "It's difficult to carve an animal."

"I do know how," said Daniel.

"Let's see if you can carve an animal," said Father, and he gave Daniel a knife like Jeff's and a block of wood.

"Winter is a good time to sit by the fire and carve something for the spring fair," said Jeff.

Every spring there was a fair in the valley. It was a time for people to meet after the long winter, and show their crafts. Sometimes people sold the things they made and other times they traded with each other. Father liked to make moccasins, so on winter nights he worked on the moccasins by the fire.

Mother started to make a quilt. She cut out pieces of cloth and sewed them together. "This will be a warm quilt for somebody's bed," she said.

287

"I'm going to carve a wooden box for the fair," said Jeff, "and make little moon decorations on the top." Jeff looked at his brother. "You haven't done anything yet with your block of wood. What are you going to carve?"

"I have to think," said Daniel. Days and days went by, then finally Daniel began to carve.

"What are you making?" asked Jeff.

"You'll see," said Daniel.

One night when Jeff looked at what Daniel was carving, he saw a neck and a head and a wing.

"Now I see it's a bird," Jeff said.

"It's a duck," said Daniel.

"You're not doing it right," said Jeff. "Its head is on backward."

"I want it that way," said Daniel, "because my duck is looking back."

"That's no way to do it," said Jeff.

Father said, "Let him do it his way."

289

Spring came, and soon it would be time for the fair. Mother had just finished her quilt, and Father had made three pairs of moccasins.

Jeff's box with carved moons on the top was finished. "This really took a long time to make," Jeff said.

"My duck took a long time, too," said Daniel.

"Are you sure you want to take that duck to the fair?" asked Jeff.

"Yes," replied Daniel.

When the day of the spring fair finally arrived, Father drove the wagon down the mountain and into town. Many people had already arrived for the fair. Father took the quilt, the moccasins, Jeff's box, and Daniel's duck to the big hall in the middle of town where the show would be held.

291

Daniel's family walked down the street in town and saw the river and talked with friends. When Father said, "Everything must be set up now in the hall," they went to the show. Handmade crafts were spread out on tables throughout the hall. There were quilts and different sizes of baskets. All the handmade dolls were on one table, and another table was filled with knitted hats.

"Did anyone notice where the wood carvings are?" asked Daniel.

"Over here," answered Jeff. They went to two tables in the center of the hall. On the small table was a carved deer. It was so beautiful that people were quiet when they looked at it. Everyone knew it had been carved by Henry Pettigrew.

All the rest of the wood carvings were on a big table. Jeff and Daniel saw the things they had carved among all the other wood carvings.

"I see my box," said Jeff.

"I see my duck," said Daniel. A group of people were looking at the table, and most of them were laughing.

"Why is everyone laughing?" asked Daniel. Jeff didn't answer. Somebody said, "Look at the duck!"

More people crowded around to look, and then they were laughing too. One person said, "That duck is so funny!"

Now Daniel understood. They were laughing at his duck. At first he wanted to run and hide, but then he felt angry. He went to the table, grabbed his duck, and ran out of the hall.

Someone was running after Daniel, but Daniel ran faster, until he came to the river. Daniel wanted to throw the duck as far as he could.

Before Daniel could throw it, a man grabbed his arm and asked, "What are you doing with that duck?"

"I'm going to throw it in the river!" said Daniel.

"You can't do that," said the man.

"I can if I want to," said Daniel. "It's my duck."

"Did you make it?" asked the man as he let go of Daniel's arm.

"Yes," said Daniel.

"Why were you going to throw it away?"

"Everybody laughed at it," Daniel said.

"Listen to me," said the man. "There are different ways of laughing. The people *liked* your duck. They laughed because they liked it."

"No! It's ugly," said Daniel.

"It isn't ugly. It's a good duck, and it made me feel happy. That's why I laughed." But the man wasn't laughing now. "You're hot and tired," he said. "Come and rest in the shade." They sat under a tree in the cool shade. "Would you sell your duck?" asked the man.

"Who would buy it?" asked Daniel.

"I might think of someone," he said.

Just then a boy and girl came walking up to them.

"How are you, Mr. Pettigrew?" they both asked.

"I'm fine," he answered, and when the boy and girl walked on, Daniel looked at the man again. "You're Henry Pettigrew!"

"Yes," he said, "and I'm a woodcarver."

"I know," said Daniel.

Daniel looked down at his duck. It wasn't ugly. It was a good duck. Henry Pettigrew had said so, and he was the best woodcarver there was in Tennessee.

Mr. Pettigrew was still looking at the duck. "Will you sell your duck to me?" Mr. Pettigrew asked.

"No," said Daniel, and he held his duck a little longer. "I will *give* my duck to you."

Comprehension Questions

1. How did Henry Pettigrew help Daniel?
2. What do you think would have happened if Mr. Pettigrew hadn't followed Daniel?

Author

Clyde Bulla began writing stories and songs in the one-room schoolhouse he went to in Missouri. He has written more than fifty books for children on many different subjects. Many have won awards. Among the books he has written are *The Sword in the Tree* and *Keep Running, Allen.*

Illustrator

Nancy Edwards Calder studied art at The Rhode Island School of Design. Her art has been used by the Smithsonian Institution in Washington, D.C. She has illustrated a book for adults about Poland long ago.

Glossary

A

active Moving much of the time; busy. *Our neighbor's new kitten is very active.*

admire Look at or think highly of. *I admire the way my uncle plays the violin.*

adult A grown-up; a person who is fully grown. *The library has books for adults and for children.*

aim To point something toward something else. *She aimed her camera at me and took a picture.*

ambulance A car that takes hurt and sick people to the hospital quickly. *The ambulance took the man to the nearest hospital.*

announcement Something told aloud to a group or put in writing and given to many people. *Our principal made an announcement that school will close early today.*

apartment A set of rooms for one household in a building or house. *My friend and I each live in an apartment but in different buildings.*

arrow A marker that shows direction. *The **arrow** on the sign pointed to the left.*

attention Careful thinking, watching, or listening. *We paid **attention** to all the directions the teacher gave us.*

B

badger A small animal with short legs that lives underground. *The **badger** dug its home under the ground.*

balcony A small place with a floor and short walls built onto the side of a house or other building. *We stood on the **balcony** and looked down onto the street.*

barn A large farm building where animals and their food are kept. *Mike went into the **barn** to see the cows.*

beach The land along the edge of a body of water, usually made of sand. *We played on the **beach** and swam in the water.*

bench A long seat for two or more people. *Judy and Rosa sat on the park **bench** and ate lunch.*

bolt Something that helps to hold things together. *Mom couldn't find the **bolt** she needed to fix the table leg.*

bounce To jump or move up and down in a lively way. *Tom **bounced** with excitement when he got the bike he wanted for his birthday.*

bowling A game played by rolling a ball at rounded, sticklike pins to push them over. *When we went bowling, I got nine out of ten pins down on my first try.*

breeze Gently moving air. *A breeze feels good on a hot summer day.*

bundle A number of things tied together. *Dora carried a bundle of wood to the fireplace.*

C

cabin A small wooden house. *We went to the beach for our vacation and stayed in a cabin.*

calm Quiet; not excited. *Jimmy seemed quite calm even though he had just won the race.*

camera Something that takes photographs or movies. *A person with a TV camera was taking pictures of the crowd for a TV show.*

castle A very large house where kings and queens lived long ago. *Hollie drew a picture of a castle that had large towers on the sides.*

chart A special drawing that shows information quickly. *Our class has a chart that tells which days our plants need to be watered.*

cloth Material made by weaving or knitting. *My cousin bought cloth to make a new dress.*

college A school some people go to after high school. *My older sister goes to college.*

community A group of people who live or work together. *Our community has a new library.*

complete To be through; finished. *She hoped to complete her report by Friday.*

conductor The person in charge of a bus or train. *The conductor took our tickets when we got on the train.*

country The land away from cities and large towns. *I like to visit my friend who lives in the country.*

cradleboard A board used for carrying a baby. *In this Indian village, the babies were carried on cradleboards.*

craft The skill of making something with one's hands. *My cousin is teaching me the craft of weaving.*

crops A large number of plants grown to be used as food. *The farmer planted crops of corn and potatoes.*

corral An area with a fence around it to help keep the animals in. *He led the animals into the corral for the night.*

cupboard A place for storing food and other household goods. *He looked in the **cupboard** for something to eat.*

D

delight To greatly please. *I was **delighted** when our team won the last game of the year.*

department A special group within a business or school. *My father works in the music **department** at the high school.*

disk A thin, flat, round thing used to store information from a computer. *After Mary worked on the computer, she put the information on a **disk**.*

distance The length of the space between two things, places, or points. *She had to travel a great **distance** to visit her uncle.*

dock A wooden floor placed over water, where people can walk and boats can tie up to load and unload. *The ferry pulled up to the **dock**, and the people got onto the boat.*

dragon A make-believe animal. *The **dragon** in the picture had a long green neck and a huge tail.*

drift Snow that has been blown into a pile. *The **drifts** of snow in front of the house were so high that we had trouble getting to the door.*

dune A hill of sand that has been piled up by the wind. *There were many **dunes** along the beach.*

E

earthquake A sudden shaking of the ground. *The earthquake made everything in the house shake.*

engineer A person who plans and builds such things as airplanes, ships, and roads. *The engineer looked at the plans for the new road.*

excuse To free from having to do something. *Today John asked to be excused early from school to go to the doctor.*

F

famous Well-known; celebrated. *I took a picture of the famous baseball player after the game.*

ferry A boat used to carry people, cars, and goods across a body of water. *We took the ferry across the river.*

flood A lot of water covering an area that usually is dry. *The heavy rains caused a flood on the farmer's fields.*

forecaster Someone who predicts what the weather will be like. *The forecaster said we should expect a thunderstorm in the morning.*

funnel A thing shaped like a V, with a large opening at the top and a small opening at the bottom. *Dad is using a funnel to pour juice from one jar into another jar.*

fur The hairy coat that covers the body of some animals, such as cats, dogs, and rabbits. *Paul petted the rabbit's soft fur.*

G

giant A very large person in a make-believe story. *The giant in the story I read was taller than the trees.*

glide To move along easily. *They watched the skater glide across the ice.*

graze To feed on growing grass. *We saw sheep grazing on the side of the hill.*

H

harmonica A small musical instrument that is played by blowing in and out through a set of holes. *Jennifer played her harmonica while I sang.*

hitch To fasten one thing to another with a rope. *The farmer hitched the horse to the wagon.*

hobby Something that a person does for fun; an interest. *Lee's hobby is making paper airplanes.*

hogan An earth-covered Indian house. *The hogan didn't have windows, but light came in through a small hole in the roof.*

honor To give special attention to someone. *The author was **honored** for the book she had written.*

hood The front, top part of a car. *To find out why the car wouldn't start, she opened the **hood.***

hospital A place where sick or hurt people go to get better. *When Mark broke his leg, he was taken to the **hospital.***

I

inch A certain length. *My finger is two **inches** long.*

information Facts. *Paula looked for **information** about how to build a birdhouse.*

insect A tiny animal with six legs and a body that has three main parts. *Some **insects** can fly.*

island Land with water all around it. *Our boat stopped at a small **island** in the middle of the river.*

K

kingdom A country that is ruled by a king or queen. *Beautiful flowers grew throughout the **kingdom.***

kneel To lean down on bent knees. *Bob **kneeled** down by the edge of the stream to get a drink of water.*

L

lightning A flash of light in the sky during a thunderstorm. *Lightning made the night sky light up during the storm.*

loom Something used for weaving cloth. *She sat at the loom all day weaving a rug.*

M

manners The proper way of acting. *Todd showed good manners by saying "please" and "thank you."*

mask Something that covers and hides the face or part of the face. *Carla had on a scary mask at the Halloween party.*

mayor The person in charge of running a city or a town. *The mayor helps decide many things that will happen in our town.*

mesa A hill with a flat top and tall sides. *We climbed to the top of the mesa and looked over the land below.*

microphone Something used to make a person's voice sound louder. *She spoke right into the microphone so the crowd would be able to hear her.*

million A very large number. *Some cities have more than a million people living in them.*

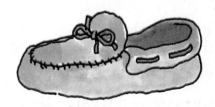

moccasin A soft leather shoe. *Moccasins are my favorite shoes.*

moose A large, heavy animal. *A big moose came out of the woods.*

mud Soft, wet earth. *There is a lot of mud along the edge of the pond.*

O

organize To put together in an orderly way. *Jill organized her flower garden so the smaller flowers would grow in front.*

P

passenger A person riding in a train, airplane, bus, ship, or car. *The conductor helped the passengers find seats on the train.*

phone Something that lets a person in one place talk to a person in another place. *The phone rang and woke me up.*

piñon A kind of pine tree. *The piñon tree gave us shade.*

plum A juicy, purple fruit. *She picked a plum from the tree and ate it.*

possum A furry animal that lives mostly in trees; also called an *opossum*. *The possum held onto the tree by its tail.*

poster A large printed sign. *A poster in our classroom shows many different kinds of farm animals.*

princess The daughter of a queen and king. *The princess lived in a castle in the huge kingdom.*

provide To give something that is needed or useful. *Rain **provides** plants with the water they need to grow.*

pucker To gather tightly together. *Max **puckered** his lips and tried to whistle.*

Q

quilt A covering for a bed. *I have a handmade **quilt** on my bed.*

R

raccoon A furry animal with black face markings that look like a mask. *The **raccoon** caught a fish.*

radish A red or white vegetable. *Clara planted **radishes** in her garden.*

rainstorm A storm with heavy rain and strong wind. *They knew a **rainstorm** was coming because the sky got dark and the wind started blowing.*

repair To fix. *We must **repair** that broken window right away.*

retire To stop working. *After teaching music for twenty-five years, he **retired**.*

rodeo A show where cowhands show different skills. *We saw a cowboy spinning a rope in the air at the **rodeo**.*

rural Of the country. *Jim is going to leave the city and move to a **rural** area.*

S

safe Free from danger. *It is not **safe** to go swimming alone.*

screwdriver A tool used to turn screws. *He used a **screwdriver** to tighten the screws on the toy car.*

seagull A bird that lives near water. *As we walked along the beach, we watched **seagulls** flying overhead.*

search To look for carefully. *She **searched** everywhere for her missing shoe.*

several More than two or three, but not many. *The library has **several** books about wildflowers.*

shack A small building that is poorly put together. *We saw a **shack** in the woods that looked as if it had been there for a long time.*

shade An area that is partly dark because light has been blocked off. *Let's sit in the **shade** of the tall tree.*

shaggy Covered with long, uneven hair. *Al brought his **shaggy** dog.*

snowstorm A storm with heavy snow and strong wind. *During the big **snowstorm**, we stayed inside.*

sofa   A long seat with a back and arms. *My mother, father, and brother were all sitting on the sofa reading the newspaper.*

spin   To turn quickly. *When he pushed on the toy top, it began to spin around in circles.*

spring   The time of year between winter and summer. *My grandfather always plants his flower garden on the first day of spring.*

sprinkler   Something that is used to spray water on the ground. *When it is hot, we like to run under the sprinkler and get wet.*

station   A place where a bus or train stops to pick up or let off passengers. *Carlos walked to the station to get the bus.*

storm   A strong wind with rain or snow. *During the storm, the tall trees bent in the wind.*

stream   A path of water that moves in one direction. *They watched the fish swim in the stream.*

stretch   To spread the arms, legs, or body to full length. *After sitting for a long time, I got up and stretched my legs.*

study To try to learn; to look at carefully. *I decided to **study** music so I can play the violin.*

suit To meet the needs of; to please. *Does it **suit** you to go to the library on Saturday?*

T

tamale A Mexican food made with dough and meat cooked in the outer covering of an ear of corn. *When we went out to eat, I had **tamales.***

tangle To become mixed together; messy. *My long hair **tangles** easily.*

tantrum A fit of anger. *When the child didn't get his way, he had a **tantrum.***

teenager A person 13 to 19 years old. *The **teenagers** put on a play for the younger children at school.*

theater A building where people go to watch movies or plays. *We went to the **theater** to see a movie about a girl and her dog.*

thunderstorm A heavy storm with thunder and lightning. *The dog hid under the bed during the **thunderstorm** because it was afraid of the loud noise.*

tornado A storm with strong winds in the shape of a funnel. *From far away, we could see the **tornado** spinning through the sky.*

trail A path made by people or animals. *They walked along the **trail** next to the stream.*

U

urban Of the city. *The **urban** community where I live has many tall buildings.*

V

valley An area of low land between mountains or hills. *My friend lives by a river in the **valley**.*

W

wag To wave from side to side or up and down. *The dog **wagged** its tail.*

warn To tell of coming danger. *We were **warned** about playing ball too close to the house.*

weather Sun, air, and water all work together to make weather. *The **weather** changed from a sunny day to a rainy, cold one.*

whirl To spin or turn suddenly. *The top **whirled** faster and faster.*

whisper To speak very softly. *He **whispered** something to his dad, and his dad smiled.*

whistle To blow through the lips and make a clear, high sound. *I **whistle** loudly when I want my dog to come.*

wrench A tool used for turning things. *I used a **wrench** to help tighten the wheel of my bicycle.*

wrong Not right. *I added the numbers many times, but I still got the **wrong** answer.*

Reading Helps

Consonants

ch	cheese	**ph**	photo	**kn**	knee
sh	sheep	**th**	think	**wr**	write

qu quiet   **squ** squirrel

br	bring	**bl**	block	**sc**	scare
cr	cross	**cl**	clown	**sk**	skate
dr	drive	**fl**	flower	**sl**	sleep
fr	frog	**gl**	glass	**sm**	smile
gr	grass	**pl**	plant	**sn**	snow
pr	pretty	**sl**	slow	**sp**	space
tr	train			**st**	story
				sw	swim

spr spring   **str** street   **thr** three

Sounds for **c**   Sounds for **g**

coat   city   game   giraffe

Vowels

Short Vowel Sounds

a ask hat
e egg set
i if six

o off top
u up bus

Long Vowel Sounds

a ate made
e eat seed
i ice five

o over rope
u use cute

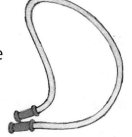

Two vowels together often stand for just one sound.

ai paint
ay play

ee feet
oa boat

Two vowels together can stand for different sounds in different words.

oo school
       book

ea head
        teach

ie tie
        chief

More Vowel Sounds

_____**y** fly   _____**y** baby

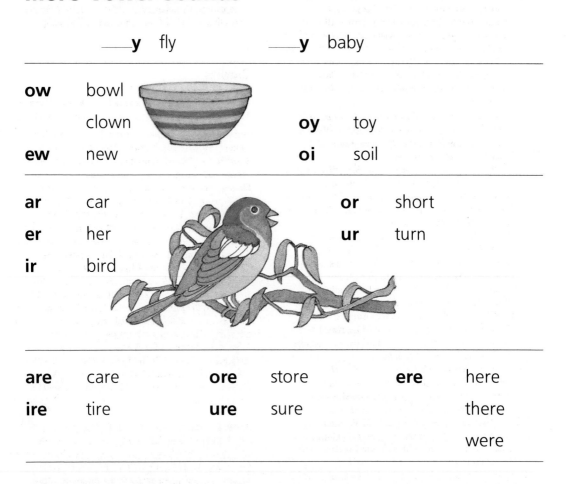

ow   bowl

          clown   **oy**   toy

ew   new   **oi**   soil

ar   car   **or**   short

er   her   **ur**   turn

ir   bird

are   care   **ore**   store   **ere**   here

ire   tire   **ure**   sure   there

                                                   were

When you come to a new word —

> **Read to the end of the sentence.**
>
> **Think about what the sentence is saying.**
>
> **Think about the sounds letters stand for.**

Does the word you named make sense in the sentence?

Does the word you named have the right sounds?

Credits